UIC The University of Illinois
at Chicago

The original edition was based on work supported by the National Science Foundation under grant
No. MDR 9050226 and the University of Illinois at Chicago. Any opinions, findings, and conclusions
or recommendations expressed in this publication are those of the author(s) and do not necessarily
reflect the views of the granting agencies.

LETTER HOME

Connections to Division

Date: _____

Dear Family Member:

In this unit, students review paper-and-pencil methods for dividing. Division is extended to two-digit divisors. Students will solve many division word problems and interpret the remainders. They will also learn strategies for solving real-world problems using a calculator and make further connections between division and fractions. Students complete an assessment activity where they will use estimation and multiplication to find the number of blades of grass in a given area.

You can help your child at home by encouraging your child to explain to you how he or she is learning to divide.

Sincerely,

_____

$$
\begin{array}{r}
22\ \text{R}3 \\
24\,\overline{)531}\quad\ \ \\
-480\quad 20 \\
\hline
51\quad\ \ \\
-\ 48\quad\ 2 \\
\hline
3\quad 22
\end{array}
$$

A method for division with a two-digit divisor

UNIT OUTLINE

Connections to Division

Pacing Suggestions

- Use the recommended number of sessions for each lesson as a guide. Students extend their division skills in this unit, but it is not necessary to stop until all students master each concept and skill. Distributed practice of small sets of division problems and sets of word problems are included in each of the succeeding units in the Daily Practice and Problems and Home Practice.

- Lesson 3 *Multiplication Methods* is an optional lesson that challenges students to learn different methods for multiplication. This lesson can be used as an extension.

Components Key: SG = Student Guide, DAB = Discovery Assignment Book, AB = Adventure Book, URG = Unit Resource Guide, and DPP = Daily Practice and Problems

	Sessions	Description	Supplies
LESSON 1			
Fractions and Division SG pages 286–293 DAB pages 151–152 URG pages 21–32 DPP A–D	2	**ACTIVITY:** Students explore the relationship between division sentences and fractions. Students use calculators to change fractions into their decimal equivalents or approximations and compare them. Repeating decimals are introduced.	• small centiwheels • calculators
LESSON 2			
Division SG pages 294–298 DAB pages 153–155 URG pages 33–45 DPP E–J	3	**ACTIVITY:** Students review a method for dividing. Estimation strategies are emphasized. Students use multiplication to check their work.	

	Sessions	Description	Supplies
LESSON 3		– OPTIONAL LESSON – EXTENSION –	
Multiplication Methods SG pages 299–303 DAB pages 157–158 URG pages 46–52	2	**OPTIONAL ACTIVITY:** Students use paper-and-pencil methods for multiplying larger numbers. A new method, lattice multiplication, is introduced. Students compare multiplication methods.	
LESSON 4			
Understanding Remainders SG pages 304–309 URG pages 53–62 DPP K–N	2	**ACTIVITY:** Students explore remainders in division problems. Students complete division problems in which the remainder is expressed as a fraction. **ASSESSMENT PAGE:** *Tie Dye T-Shirts,* Unit Resource Guide, page 60.	
LESSON 5			
Calculator Strategies: Division SG pages 310–313 URG pages 63–69 DPP O–P	1	**ACTIVITY:** Students use calculators to divide larger numbers. They divide money using a calculator so that the quotient reflects both dollars and cents.	• calculators
LESSON 6			
Grass Act SG page 314 URG pages 70–84 DPP Q–T	2	**ASSESSMENT ACTIVITY:** Students solve an open-ended problem and write their solution strategies. They estimate the number of blades of grass in a given area. **ASSESSMENT PAGE:** *Grass Act Questions,* Unit Resource Guide, page 83.	• scissors • calculators • index cards • rulers • grassy area or sod, nylon netting, screen, or towel

CONNECTIONS

A current list of connections is available at www.kendallhunt.com.

Literature   **Suggested Title**

- Wilder, Laura Ingalls. *Little House in the Big Woods.* HarperCollins, New York, 2001.

Software

- *Comparing with Ratios* introduces students to recognizing and using ratios.
- *Fraction Attraction* develops understanding of fractions using fraction bars, pie charts, hundreds blocks, and other materials.
- *Fraction Operation* develops conceptual understanding of fraction operations, including finding common denominators.
- *How the West was One + Three × Four* provides practice with the order of operations.
- *Math Munchers Deluxe* provides practice in basic facts and finding equivalent fractions, decimals, percents, ratios, angles and identifying geometric shapes, factors and multiples in an arcade-like game.
- *Mighty Math Calculating Crew* poses short answer questions about number operations, 3-dimensional shapes, and money skills.
- *Mighty Math Number Heroes* poses short answer questions about fractions, number operations, polygons, and probability.

BACKGROUND

Connections to Division

"Instructional programs from prekindergarten to grade 12 should enable all students to compute fluently and make reasonable estimates.

"Developing fluency requires a balance and connection between conceptual understanding and computational proficiency. On the one hand, computational methods that are over-practiced without understanding are often forgotten or remembered incorrectly (Hiebert 1999; Kamii, Lewis, and Livingston, 1993; Hiebert and Lindquist 1990). On the other hand, understanding without fluency can inhibit the problem-solving process (Thornton 1990).

"Part of being able to compute fluently means making smart choices about which tools to use and when. Students should have experiences that help them learn to choose among mental computation, paper-and-pencil strategies, estimation, and calculator use. The particular context, the question, and the numbers involved all play roles in those choices. Do the numbers allow a mental strategy? Does the context call for an estimate? Does the problem require repeated and tedious computations? Students should evaluate problem situations to determine whether an estimate or an exact answer is needed, using their number sense to advantage, and be able to give a rationale for their decision."

From the National Council of Teachers of Mathematics *Principles and Standards for School Mathematics,* 2000.

The activities in this unit reinforce students' conceptual understanding of division. Children further investigate how fractions and division connect and how to interpret division done on a calculator. Fluency with division using a paper-and-pencil method does not ensure that students will know when to use division. Therefore, a variety of problem contexts are provided in which division is the most efficient operation for finding a solution to the problem.

Since problems are presented in contexts, students must use the information given to decide how the remainder should be interpreted. They also learn to express a quotient as a mixed number. The forgiving method, the paper-and-pencil method for division discussed in Unit 4, is reviewed and extended to include two-digit divisors. Students are encouraged to continue to use mental math to divide round numbers and to use efficient estimation strategies as they divide larger numbers.

As students solve problems involving larger numbers, they need to develop facility with calculators.

Using calculators requires that students understand the arithmetic processes called for in each situation. They must also use estimation to determine if the solution shown on the calculator display is reasonable. The use of calculators also provides students with the resources needed to solve more interesting and complex problems efficiently.

This unit provides many practice problems for multiplying and dividing. These should be assigned conservatively. It is better for children to do a few problems at a time so that they have time to think and internalize the concepts behind the computations.

Students review paper-and-pencil multiplication in the context of checking division. In an optional activity, students can extend their knowledge of multiplication by learning a classic method called lattice multiplication. This method has been known and used for over 500 years. Students also use multiplication in an open-ended assessment problem that requires problem-solving, estimation, and communication skills.

Resources

- Burns, Marilyn. *About Teaching Mathematics. A K–8 Resource.* Math Solutions Publications, White Plains, NY, 1992.

- Hiebert, James. "Relationships between Research and the NCTM Standards." *Journal for Research in Mathematics Education* 30, pp. 3–19, January 1999.

- Hiebert, James, and Mary Lindquist. "Developing Mathematical Knowledge in the Young Child" in *Mathematics for the Young Child,* edited by Joseph N. Payne, pp. 17–36. Reston, VA: National Council of Teachers of Mathematics, 1990.

- Kamii, Constance, Barbara A. Lewis, and Sally Jones Livingston. "Primary Arithmetic: Children Inventing Their Own Procedures." *Arithmetic Teacher* 41, pp. 200–203, December 1993.

- *Principles and Standards for School Mathematics,* The National Council of Teachers of Mathematics, Reston, VA, 2000.

- Thornton, Carol A. "Strategies for the Basic Facts" in *Mathematics for the Young Child,* edited by Joseph N. Payne, pp. 133–51. National Council of Teachers of Mathematics, Reston, VA, 1990.

Assessment Indicators

- Can students divide with 2-digit divisors using paper and pencil?
- Can students estimate quotients?
- Can students interpret remainders?
- Can students write quotients as mixed numbers?
- Can students use a calculator to solve division problems?
- Can students check division using multiplication?
- Can students solve open-ended problems and communicate solution strategies?
- Can students find decimal equivalents for fractions?

OBSERVATIONAL ASSESSMENT RECORD

(A1) Can students divide with 2-digit divisors using paper and pencil?

(A2) Can students estimate quotients?

(A3) Can students interpret remainders?

(A4) Can students write quotients as mixed numbers?

(A5) Can students use a calculator to solve division problems?

(A6) Can students check division using multiplication?

(A7) Can students solve open-ended problems and communicate solution strategies?

(A8) Can students find decimal equivalents for fractions?

(A9) _____

Name	A1	A2	A3	A4	A5	A6	A7	A8	A9	Comments
1.										
2.										
3.										
4.										
5.										
6.										
7.										
8.										
9.										
10.										
11.										
12.										
13.										

Name	A1	A2	A3	A4	A5	A6	A7	A8	A9	Comments
14.										
15.										
16.										
17.										
18.										
19.										
20.										
21.										
22.										
23.										
24.										
25.										
26.										
27.										
28.										
29.										
30.										
31.										
32.										

⁹ Daily Practice and Problems

Connections to Division

A DPP Menu for Unit 9

Eight icons designate the subject matter of the DPP items. Each DPP item may fall into one or more of the categories listed below. The icons appear in the Teacher Notes column in each of the DPP items. Below is a brief menu of the DPP items included in Unit 9.

N Number Sense C, E–G, I, L–R, T	**Computation** A, C, H, J, L–R, T	**Time** B	**Geometry**
Math Facts G, K, M, Q, S	**$ Money** C, H	**Measurement** H	**Data** D

Two DPP items are included for each class session listed in the Unit Outline. The first item is always a Bit and the second is either a Task or a Challenge. The *Daily Practice and Problems and Home Practice Guide* in the *Teacher Implementation Guide* includes information on how and when to use the DPP. A *Scope and Sequence Chart* for the Daily Practice and Problems for the year can also be found in the *Teacher Implementation Guide*.

Review of Math Facts

In the first half of the year, DPP items reviewed the multiplication and division facts through work with fact families (e.g., $3 \times 5 = 15$ and $5 \times 3 = 15$, so $15 \div 3 = 5$ and $15 \div 5 = 3$). Students will continue to review the facts as part of the Daily Practice and Problems.

The table below lists the groups of facts and indicates when each is studied throughout the DPP in Units 9–16.

The DPP for this unit reviews the facts for the 5s and 10s. See Items G, K, M, Q, and S.

For a detailed explanation of our approach to learning the facts, see the *Grade 5 Facts Resource Guide* and the TIMS Tutor: *Math Facts* in the *Teacher Implementation Guide*. Also, see the *Math Facts Philosophy: Information for Parents,* which can be found immediately following the Unit 2 Background.

Unit	Distribution of Multiplication and Division Facts
9	5s and 10s
10	2s and squares
11	3s and 9s
12	Last six facts
13	2s, 5s, 10s, and squares
14	3s, 9s, and last six facts
15	Review all facts.
16	Review all facts.

Students may solve the items individually, in groups, or as a class. The items may also be assigned for homework.

Student Questions	Teacher Notes

 Division Practice

Use paper and pencil or mental math to solve the following problems. Estimate to be sure your answer is reasonable.

   A. $678 \div 4 =$

   B. $200 \div 5 =$

   C. $56 \div 5 =$

   D. $1264 \div 8 =$

 TIMS Bit

A. 169 R2

B. 40

C. 11 R1

D. 158

 Arrival Time

Los Angeles is in the Pacific Standard Time (PST) zone and New York is in the Eastern Standard Time (EST) zone. When it is noon in Los Angeles, it is 3:00 P.M. in New York.

A plane left New York at 8:30 A.M. and took 5 hours to fly to Los Angeles. The time in Los Angeles is always 3 hours earlier than New York. What time will the plane arrive in Los Angeles?

TIMS Task

10:30 A.M.

Time change is a difficult concept for some students. Looking at a time zone map of the United States will help. Daylight savings time further complicates the idea because not all areas of the U.S. change their clocks. Ignore this fact for this problem.

Bargain Shopping

Frank needs to buy school supplies. He needs four of each item. For each item, help Frank figure out whether he will save money by buying the items in packs or individually. Figure out how much he will save on each item. Then, find his total savings.

Item	Packs of 4	Individual
pencils	18¢	4¢
rulers	98¢	25¢
folders	45¢	12¢
crayons	29¢	7¢
pens	$1.40	36¢

TIMS Bit

pencils—individual; savings of 2¢

rulers—pack; savings of 2¢

folders—pack; savings of 3¢

crayons—individual; savings of 1¢

pens—pack; savings of 4¢

Total savings of 12¢.

 Arranging Colors

Lee Yah received three different-colored sweatshirts for her birthday—blue, red, and yellow. She is deciding which one to wear to school on Monday, Tuesday, and Wednesday.

1. In what order can she wear the three sweatshirts? List all the different ways.

2. If Lee Yah decides to wear the blue sweatshirt on Monday, in what order can she wear the other two shirts? List all the possibilities.

3. If she chooses not to wear the blue and yellow sweatshirts in a row (not blue, yellow and not yellow, blue), in what order could she wear the three sweatshirts? List all the different ways.

TIMS Challenge

1. 6 ways: RYB, RBY, BYR, BRY, YRB, YBR

2. 2 ways: YR or RY

3. 2 ways: BRY or YRB

Estimating with Ease

See if you can figure out these problems in your head. Then, write down your reasoning for each answer.

1. About how many 12s are in 140?

2. About how many 25s are in 370?

3. About how many 20s are in 345?

TIMS Bit

Answers will vary but should include students' thinking strategies. Sharing these strategies with the class, or in groups, will allow students to see several ways of figuring estimates.

1. 10 or 11 are good estimates.

2. 14 or 15 are good estimates. $25 \times 10 = 250$ Then, skip count by 25s—275, 300, 325, 350—for a total of fourteen 25s. Alternatively, there are four 25s in 100 so there are twelve 25s in 300. Add on three more 25s for a total of 15 $(300 + 25 + 25 + 25 = 375)$.

3. 15, 16, or 17 are good estimates. There are five 20s in 100 so there are fifteen 20s in 300. It takes 2 more 20s to reach 340 for a total of 17. Alternatively, $20 \times 10 = 200$ and $20 \times 20 = 400$. Since 345 is about halfway between 200 and 400, 15 is a good estimate.

Tenths, Hundredths, and Thousandths

One example is provided for each. Encourage students to use grids from Unit 7 or picture them in their minds.

1. Name a decimal that is greater than 0.3 but less than 0.35.

    1. 0.33

2. Name a decimal that is greater than 0.25 but less than 0.26.

    2. 0.254

3. Name a decimal that is greater than 0.403 but less than 0.41.

    3. .409

4. Name a fraction that is greater than $\frac{57}{100}$ but less than $\frac{7}{10}$.

    4. $\frac{6}{10}$ or $\frac{60}{100}$

5. Name a fraction that is greater than $\frac{8}{16}$ but less than 0.8.

    5. $\frac{7}{10}$

6. Name a fraction that is greater than 17% but less than 0.2.

    6. $\frac{18}{100}$

Practicing the Facts

TIMS Bit

A. $300 \div 50 =$

A. 6

B. $400 \div 4 =$

B. 100

C. $150 \div 3 =$

C. 50

D. $100 \div 10 =$

D. 10

E. $45 \div 5 =$

E. 9

F. $2500 \div 5 =$

F. 500

G. $600 \div 100 =$

G. 6

H. $35 \div 7 =$

H. 5

I. $10 \div 5 =$

I. 2

Craft Fair

1. Lee Yah and Manny are setting up tables for the fifth-grade family craft show. Each table is 200 cm long. Tables will line up along two sides of the room which measure 12 meters each. Each participant who wishes to sell crafts pays a $15 rental fee for one table or $25 for two tables. Mr. Moreno tells the students that all the tables have been rented. Only 2 people rented two tables. How much money will the school make on the craft show?

2. The community craft show will be held in the gym next month. The school is charging $25 for one table and will have five times as many tables as the fifth-grade craft show. How much will the school make for hosting the community craft show if all of the tables are rented?

1. $170; There are 12 tables.
   8 people pay $15.
   2 people pay $25.

2. $1500

 Fractions, Decimals, and the Calculator

TIMS Bit

Use a calculator to change each of the following fractions to decimals. Then, compare the decimals to see if each pair of fractions are equivalent.

A. $\frac{4}{7}$ and $\frac{3}{5}$

B. $\frac{1}{3}$ and $\frac{13}{39}$

C. $\frac{12}{15}$ and $\frac{8}{11}$

A. $\frac{4}{7} \neq \frac{3}{5}$ since $\frac{4}{7} \approx .57$ and $\frac{3}{5} = .6$

B. $\frac{1}{3} = \frac{13}{39}$

C. $\frac{12}{15} \neq \frac{8}{11}$ since $\frac{12}{15} = .8$ and $\frac{8}{11} \approx .73$

Division Practice

Use estimation to help you divide. Use a paper-and-pencil method or mental math. Show how you check your work.

A. $23\overline{)756}$ B. $20\overline{)4000}$

C. $42\overline{)8973}$ D. $75\overline{)684}$

TIMS Task

A. 32 R20
$32 \times 23 + 20 = 756$

B. 200
$20 \times 200 = 4000$

C. 213 R27
$213 \times 42 + 27 = 8973$

D. 9 R9
$9 \times 75 + 9 = 684$

K **More Fact Practice**

Find n to make each number sentence true.

A. $n \times 5 = 40$ B. $n \times 7 = 70$

C. $n \div 4 = 5$ D. $80 \div n = 10$

E. $10 \times n = 50$ F. $30 \div 5 = n$

G. $9 \times 10 = n$ H. $15 \div n = 5$

I. $n \times 8 = 80$

TIMS Bit

A. 8	B. 10
C. 20	D. 8
E. 5	F. 6
G. 90	H. 3
I. 10	

Digits Game: **Addition with Decimals**

TIMS Task

Draw boxes like these on your paper.

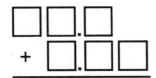

As your teacher or classmate chooses digits from a deck of digit cards, place them in the boxes. Try to make the largest sum. Remember that each digit will be read only once. Once you place a digit, it cannot be moved.

To begin the game, students draw the set of boxes on their papers. The teacher chooses a digit at random from a set of *Digit Cards (0–9)*. (*Digit Cards* can be found in the Generic Section of the *Unit Resource Guide*. As an alternative, you can use a deck of playing cards. The ace can stand for 1 and the joker or a face card can stand for zero.) Students place the digit in a box in such a way as to try to get the largest sum. Once a digit is placed, it cannot be moved. Then, the teacher chooses a second digit without replacing the first to the deck. Play continues until the teacher has read enough digits to fill the boxes. The player with the largest sum wins. Play again; however, this time students try to make the smallest sum.

 Multiplying and Dividing by Multiples of Ten

TIMS Bit

A. 80 × 500 =

B. 60 × 100 =

C. 20 × 5000 =

D. 3000 ÷ 60 =

E. 70,000 ÷ 100 =

F. 4500 ÷ 90 =

A. 40,000

B. 6000

C. 100,000

D. 50

E. 700

F. 50

Operations

Use paper and pencil or mental math, not your calculator, to solve these problems. Write any remainders as whole numbers. When you finish a problem, look back to see if your answer is reasonable.

A. $59 \times 14 =$

B. $86 \times 42 =$

C. $409 \times 4 =$

D. $2486 \div 4 =$

E. $2486 \div 14 =$

F. $1067 \div 37 =$

TIMS Task

A. 826

B. 3612

C. 1636

D. 621 R2

E. 177 R8

F. 28 R31

 Estimate the Products

Estimate the products. Be prepared to share how you estimated.

A. $4.2 \times 53 =$

B. $0.63 \times 0.18 =$

C. $0.25 \times 119 =$

D. $19 \times 81.56 =$

E. $2.09 \times 3.982 =$

F. $66 \times 9.09 =$

TIMS Bit

Accept all reasonable answers. It's important for students to hear how other students estimate. One possible estimate is listed for each.

A. $4 \times 50 = 200$

B. $\frac{1}{2}$ of 0.18 is 0.09

C. $\frac{1}{4}$ of 120 is 30

D. $20 \times 80 = 1600$

E. $2 \times 4 = 8$

F. $66 \times 10 = 660$

Digits Game: **Subtraction with Decimals**

Draw boxes like these on your paper.

As your teacher or classmate chooses digits from a deck of digit cards, place them in the boxes. Try to make the largest difference. Remember that each digit will be read only once. Once you place a digit, it cannot be moved.

TIMS Task

To begin the game, students draw the set of boxes on their paper. The teacher chooses a digit at random from a set of *Digit Cards* (0–9). (*Digit Cards* can be found in the Generic Section of the *Unit Resource Guide.* As an alternative, you can use a deck of playing cards. The ace can stand for 1 and the joker or a face card can stand for zero.) Students place the digit in a box in such a way as to try to get the largest difference. Once a digit is placed, it cannot be moved. Then, the teacher chooses a second digit without replacing the first to the deck. Play continues until the teacher has read enough digits to fill the boxes. The player with the largest difference wins. Play again; however, this time students try to make the smallest difference.

Q **Dividing by Multiples of Ten**

A. $9000 \div 100 =$

B. $45{,}000 \div 900 =$

C. $20{,}000 \div 2 =$

D. $350 \div 70 =$

E. $250{,}000 \div 500 =$

F. $30{,}000 \div 30 =$

TIMS Bit

A. 90

B. 50

C. 10,000

D. 5

E. 500

F. 1000

Thinking about Remainders

1. You are dividing a number by 6 and at the end of the problem your remainder is 7. What does that mean?

2. Make a list of the possible remainders you can have when you are finished dividing a number by 8.

1. It means that 6 can be divided into the dividend 1 more time. You are not finished dividing.

2. 0–7

 Reviewing Division Facts: 5s and 10s

A. $45 \div 5 =$ B. $25 \div 5 =$

C. $10 \div 2 =$ D. $60 \div 10 =$

E. $40 \div 8 =$ F. $30 \div 3 =$

G. $20 \div 5 =$ H. $80 \div 10 =$

I. $30 \div 6 =$ J. $35 \div 5 =$

K. $15 \div 3 =$ L. $50 \div 10 =$

M. $70 \div 10 =$ N. $90 \div 9 =$

O. $40 \div 4 =$ P. $20 \div 2 =$

Q. $100 \div 10 =$

TIMS Bit

A. 9	B. 5
C. 5	D. 6
E. 5	F. 10
G. 4	H. 8
I. 5	J. 7
K. 5	L. 5
M. 7	N. 10
O. 10	P. 10
Q. 10	

Student Questions | **Teacher Notes**

 Remainders

1. Solve each of the following problems. Each one has a remainder. Write the quotient three ways: with a whole number remainder, as a mixed number, and as a decimal.

   A. $6 \div 4 =$ B. $19 \div 4 =$

   C. $49 \div 4 =$

2. Choose one of the problems. Write 3 different stories for the problem showing how you might use each of the three types of quotients.

TIMS Challenge

Students will need calculators to complete this challenge.

1. A. 1 R2; $1\frac{1}{2}$; 1.5

   B. 4 R3; $4\frac{3}{4}$; 4.75

   C. 12 R1; $12\frac{1}{4}$; 12.25

2. One possible answer is given.

$6 \div 4 = 1$ R2; To share 6 pencils among 4 students you would need to give each student 1 pencil. Two pencils would be left over.

$6 \div 4 = 1\frac{1}{2}$; To share 6 cookies among 4 students you could give each student $1\frac{1}{2}$ cookies.

$6 \div 4 = 1.5$; To share $6 among 4 students, you would need to give each student $1.50.

LESSON GUIDE

Fractions and Division

Estimated Class Sessions: 2

Students use pictures to explore the relationship between fractions and division. They use the small centiwheel and a calculator to find decimal equivalents (or decimal approximations) for fractions.

Key Content

- Interpreting fractions as division.
- Finding decimal equivalents (or decimal approximations) for fractions using the small centiwheel.
- Finding decimal equivalents (or decimal approximations) for fractions using calculators.
- Identifying repeating decimals.

Key Vocabulary

repeating decimals

Daily Practice and Problems: Bits for Lesson 1

A. Division Practice (URG p. 10)

Use paper and pencil or mental math to solve the following problems. Estimate to be sure your answer is reasonable.

A. $678 \div 4 =$

B. $200 \div 5 =$

C. $56 \div 5 =$

D. $1264 \div 8 =$

C. Bargain Shopping (URG p. 11)

Frank needs to buy school supplies. He needs four of each item. For each item, help Frank figure out whether he will save money by buying the items in packs or individually. Figure out how much he will save on each item. Then, find his total savings.

Item	Packs of 4	Individual
pencils	18¢	4¢
rulers	98¢	25¢
folders	45¢	12¢
crayons	29¢	7¢
pens	$1.40	36¢

DPP Task and Challenge are on page 27. Suggestions for using the DPPs are on page 27.

Curriculum Sequence

Before This Unit

Fractions and Decimals. In Units 3 and 5, students developed fraction concepts and skills using a variety of concrete models, including rectangles on dot paper. Students used concrete models to make connections between fractions and decimals in Unit 7. In Unit 7 Lesson 1, they used centiwheels to find decimal equivalents (or decimal approximations) for fractions.

After This Unit

Students will explore multiplying fractions in Unit 12.

Materials List

Print Materials for Students

	Math Facts and Daily Practice and Problems	Activity	Homework
Student Guide (Student Books)		*Fractions and Division* Pages 286–292	*Fractions and Division* Homework Section Page 293
Discovery Assignment Book (Student Books)			Home Practice Part 1 Page 147 and *Dividing Pizzas* Pages 151–152
Unit Resource Guide (Teacher Resources)	DPP Items A–D Pages 10–11 ⊙	*Small Centiwheels* Unit 7 Lesson 1, Page 43, 1 wheel per student (optional)	
Generic Section (Teacher Resources) ⊙		*Centimeter Dot Paper,* 1 per student (optional)	

⊙ *available on Teacher Resource CD*

All Transparency Masters, Blackline Masters, and Assessment Blackline Masters in the Unit Resource Guide are on the Teacher Resource CD.

Supplies for Each Student

calculator
small centiwheel

Before the Activity

If students no longer have their small centiwheels, make new ones for students using the *Small Centiwheels* Activity Page in the Unit 7 Lesson 1 Lesson Guide.

Developing the Activity

Part 1. Fractions and Division

Read the vignette on the *Fractions and Division* Activity Pages in the *Student Guide.* Students in small groups should discuss strategies for sharing 2 brownies among 3 boys. Encourage students to use various tools such as rectangles on dot paper or calculators.

Question 1 shows one strategy for dividing the brownies (see Figure 1). Note that we draw 3 × 4 rectangles on dot paper here. Students can also use 1 × 3 rectangles for this problem but a 3 × 4 rectangle will work for *Question 2* as well. There are other ways to divide the brownies.

Figure 1: *Dividing two brownies among three boys—each boy gets $\frac{2}{3}$ of a brownie.*

Question 2 asks students to divide the two brownies among four boys and show their solutions in a drawing using two rectangles. (Drawing their rectangles on dot paper as they did in Unit 5 may be helpful to students or students may choose to simply sketch rectangles and show possible divisions.) A solution drawn on dot paper is shown in Figure 2. Discuss the fractions represented by the students' pictures.

Figure 2: *Dividing two brownies among four boys—each boy gets $\frac{2}{4}$ of a brownie.*

Ask students to use rectangles to find other possible strategies they can use to divide two brownies among four boys. Make sure students understand that the

---

Fractions and Division

Edward and Brandon walk into the lunch room. Edward says, "My mom packed 2 brownies in my lunch today. I'll share them with you if you want."

"Sure," Brandon replies. "We can each have one brownie then."

As the boys sit down, Romesh walks over and joins them. "Those brownies look great. How about sharing them with me, please?"

"Okay, but how can we share them equally?" Edward asks.

 Discuss

1. Think about how the three boys can share the two brownies equally. One solution is to divide each brownie into three equal pieces. You can show this using rectangles on dot paper.

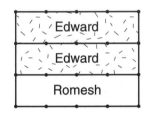

   A. How many pieces will each boy get?
   B. What fraction of 1 whole brownie does this represent?

Student Guide - Page 286

---

2. A. Nicholas joins the boys at their table. They decide to split the 2 brownies among the four boys. Draw rectangles to show how you can divide 2 brownies among the four boys.
   B. If they divide each brownie into four equal pieces, how many pieces will each boy get?
   C. What fraction of one whole brownie does this represent?
   D. Using rectangles, find another way to divide the two brownies among 4 boys.

A fraction is also a way to show division. The fraction line or bar means you divide the numerator by the denominator. For example, $\frac{2}{3}$ means 2 divided by 3. We can write this as a division number sentence:

$$\frac{2}{3} = 2 \div 3$$

 Explore

The following chart illustrates what happens when 2 brownies are shared with more and more people.

Sharing Brownies

Number of Brownies	Number of Boys	Number of Brownies Each Boy Will Get	Division Number Sentence
2	1	$\frac{2 \text{ brownies}}{1 \text{ boy}}=$ 2 brownies per boy	$2 \div 1 = 2$
2	2	$\frac{2 \text{ brownies}}{2 \text{ boys}}=$ 1 brownie per boy	$2 \div 2 = 1$
2	3	$\frac{2 \text{ brownies}}{3 \text{ boys}}=$ $\frac{2}{3}$ of a brownie per boy	$2 \div 3 = \frac{2}{3}$
2	4	$\frac{2 \text{ brownies}}{4 \text{ boys}}=$ $\frac{2}{4}$ of a brownie per boy	$2 \div 4 = \frac{2}{4}$
2	5	?	?

Student Guide - Page 287

3. A. If Edward divides his 2 brownies among 5 people, what fraction of a brownie will each person get?

 B. Write the division number sentence that this fraction represents. Use the boxes as a guide.

$$\frac{\square}{\square} = \square \div \square$$

4. A. Brandon's mother packed 6 cookies in his lunch. How can Brandon share his six cookies with Edward, Romesh, and Nicholas? (*Note:* The 6 cookies will be divided among 4 boys.)

 B. 6 cookies ÷ 4 boys = ? Draw circles to represent the 6 cookies. Show how Brandon can divide the cookies fairly among the 4 boys. How many will each of the four boys get?

 C. What are other names for this number?

Discuss ─────────────────────

Decimals

We can use a calculator to change fractions to decimals.

5. Jackie shares her apple with Nila. If they share it fairly, how much apple will each girl get?

Each girl will get $\frac{1}{2}$ of the apple. This fraction means 1 apple divided between 2 girls or 1 ÷ 2. Use your calculator to find a decimal equivalent to $\frac{1}{2}$ by pressing [1] [÷] [2] [=]. You should see 0.5 on your calculator. This tells you that 0.5 is equal to $\frac{1}{2}$. Notice that $\frac{1}{2} + \frac{1}{2} = 1$ just as 0.5 + 0.5 = 1.

288 SG · Grade 5 · Unit 9 · Lesson 1   Fractions and Division

Student Guide - Page 288

TIMS Tip

Some students may still need to use drawings of rectangles to show the division problem in *Question 3*. Students should be encouraged to use this strategy as needed.

Each boy will receive $1\frac{1}{2}$ cookies.

Figure 4: *Dividing six cookies among four boys*

TIMS Tip

Students should use the division key on their calculators that results in decimal answers and not use integer division.

24   URG · Grade 5 · Unit 9 · Lesson 1

---

amount of brownie that each boy receives will not change, but the fraction name may change. For example, $\frac{2}{4}$ of a brownie is the same as $\frac{1}{2}$ of the brownie.

Ask students how the four boys can divide the brownies evenly if they have already cut them into three pieces as shown in *Question 1*. One solution is to give each boy $\frac{2}{6} + \frac{1}{6}$ of a brownie as shown in Figure 3.

Figure 3: *Each of the 4 boys gets $\frac{2}{6} + \frac{1}{6}$ or $\frac{1}{2}$ of a brownie.*

After these two questions have been discussed, connect fractions to division. Ask:

- *Which operation did the boys use to share the brownies: addition, subtraction, multiplication, or division?* (Students should realize that the boys were dividing. Explain that the line which divides the numerator and the denominator means that you can divide the numerator by the denominator.)

Students use the Sharing Brownies data table to answer *Question 3*. If 2 brownies are divided among 5 people, each person will get $\frac{2}{5}$ of a brownie. We can write the following division number sentence: $2 \div 5 = \frac{2}{5}$.

In *Question 4,* students divide six cookies among four boys. They can draw circles to represent the cookies. Ask them to explore the different ways these cookies can be divided. One possible way is shown in Figure 4. Alternatively, the problem can be solved by using division.

$\frac{6 \text{ cookies}}{4 \text{ boys}}$ or $6 \div 4 = \frac{6}{4}$

Discuss the division with students. Students should find that each boy will receive $1\frac{1}{2}$ cookies. They should recognize different names for $1\frac{1}{2}$, including $\frac{3}{2}$ and $\frac{6}{4}$ and 1.5.

Once students understand these concepts, assign the *Dividing Pizzas* Homework Pages in the *Discovery Assignment Book*.

Part 2. Decimals

Students use the Decimals section of the *Fractions and Division* Activity Pages in the *Student Guide* for this part of the lesson. Each student will need a small centiwheel and calculator to complete this section.

In the first part of **Question 5,** students should recognize that if 2 girls split 1 apple, each girl gets $\frac{1}{2}$ of the apple. Students then use division on their calculators to find a decimal equivalent for $\frac{1}{2}$ ($1 \div 2 = 0.5$).

Question 6 gives students further practice with tenths. Students draw a picture showing how four granola bars can be equally divided among five children. See Figure 5 for one solution. They are then asked to use a calculator to find the decimal equivalent for this fraction. Check to be sure that students are using their calculators correctly. Students should be able to read 0.8 (eight-tenths) accurately and connect 0.8 to $\frac{4}{5}$. Point out that $0.8 + 0.8 + 0.8 + 0.8 + 0.8$ or $0.8 \times 5 = 4$ on the calculator.

Each child will receive $\frac{4}{5}$ or 0.8 of a granola bar.

Figure 5: *Dividing four granola bars among five children*

Four boys share one pizza in **Question 7.** Students should recognize that each boy will receive $\frac{1}{4}$ of the pizza. Ask students to find the decimal equivalent for $\frac{1}{4}$. Using what they have learned in Unit 7, many students will recognize that $\frac{1}{4} = 0.25$ without using their calculators.

Question 8 asks students to use a calculator to find the decimal equivalent for $\frac{1}{8}$. Make sure that students can read the 0.125 accurately as one hundred twenty-five thousandths.

Students can complete **Questions 9–10** with a partner. Each student should complete the calculator work independently and then compare his or her results with those of another student before proceeding. Take some time to explore the relationship between the fractions and their decimal equivalents. For example, $\frac{3}{4}$ is the same as $3 \times \frac{1}{4}$ and 0.75 is the same as 3×0.25.

TIMS Tip

Encourage students to make connections between the fractions and their decimal equivalents. They can make visual representations using centiwheels. They can also connect the decimals to money. For example, a quarter ($\frac{1}{4}$) of a dollar is $0.25.

---

6. **A.** Felicia has 4 granola bars to share among 5 children. Use rectangles to show how Felicia can divide the four granola bars among 5 people.

   B. What fraction of one granola bar will each child get?

   C. Use your calculator to find the decimal equivalent. What are other names for this number?

   D. Complete this number sentence: $0.8 = \frac{?}{5}$

7. **A.** Frank, Roberto, Michael, and Manny share one pizza. What fraction of the pizza will each boy get?

   B. Use your calculator to find the decimal equivalent.

   C. What are other names for this number?

8. **A.** Shannon's mother baked a pie. She cut the pie into 8 equal pieces. Each piece is what fraction of the pie?

   B. Use your calculator to find a decimal for this fraction.

   C. What are other names for this number?

   D. Complete the following number sentence: $\frac{1}{8} = \frac{?}{1000}$

9. Draw this table on your paper. Use your calculator to change each fraction into a decimal. Write the decimal exactly as it is shown in your calculator's window. Complete the table.

Fraction	Decimal
$\frac{1}{10}$	
$\frac{1}{8}$	
$\frac{1}{4}$	
$\frac{1}{3}$	
$\frac{2}{4}$	
$\frac{1}{2}$	0.5
$\frac{2}{3}$	
$\frac{3}{4}$	
1	1.0
$\frac{9}{8}$	
$\frac{5}{4}$	
$\frac{14}{10}$	

Student Guide - Page 289

---

10. **A.** Look at the decimal for $\frac{1}{3}$. What do you notice about this decimal?

    B. $\frac{1}{2}$ and 0.5 are equal. Are $\frac{1}{3}$ and 0.3333333 equal?

    If your calculator had more space in the window, the 3's would continue to repeat. Decimals which have digits that repeat are called **repeating decimals**. Your calculator cannot give an exact decimal equivalent for $\frac{1}{3}$, but 0.333333333 is a very close approximation. We use the symbol $\approx$ to show that 0.333333333 is approximately equal to $\frac{1}{3}$.
    $$\frac{1}{3} \approx 0.333333333$$

    C. Use the fraction circle that is divided into thirds and your small centiwheel to find a decimal for $\frac{1}{3}$ (to the nearest hundredth).

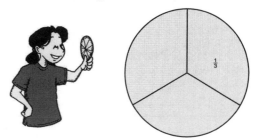

11. **A.** Look at the decimal for $\frac{2}{3}$ in the table you completed for Question 9. What number continues to repeat?

    B. What is the last digit in the decimal for $\frac{2}{3}$ shown on your calculator?

    C. Complete this number sentence: $\frac{2}{3} \approx ?$

    D. Place your centiwheel on top of the circle. Use your centiwheel and the circle divided into thirds to find a decimal for $\frac{2}{3}$ (to the nearest hundredth).

Student Guide - Page 290

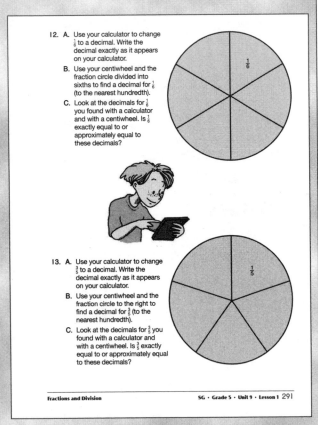

12. A. Use your calculator to change $\frac{1}{6}$ to a decimal. Write the decimal exactly as it appears on your calculator.

B. Use your centiwheel and the fraction circle divided into sixths to find a decimal for $\frac{1}{6}$ (to the nearest hundredth).

C. Look at the decimals for $\frac{1}{6}$ you found with a calculator and with a centiwheel. Is $\frac{1}{6}$ exactly equal to or approximately equal to these decimals?

13. A. Use your calculator to change $\frac{3}{5}$ to a decimal. Write the decimal exactly as it appears on your calculator.

B. Use your centiwheel and the fraction circle to the right to find a decimal for $\frac{3}{5}$ (to the nearest hundredth).

C. Look at the decimals for $\frac{3}{5}$ you found with a calculator and with a centiwheel. Is $\frac{3}{5}$ exactly equal to or approximately equal to these decimals?

Fractions and Division   SG · Grade 5 · Unit 9 · Lesson 1 291

Student Guide - Page 291

Content Note

Some calculators are able to display up to 10 digits in their window. When an answer results in more than 10 digits, the calculator stores more than 10 digits in its memory. The number in the window is rounded to 10 digits.

Journal Prompt

What are some advantages to expressing fractions as decimals?

Students will need small centiwheels to complete *Questions 10–14.* You may need to review how to use a centiwheel to find a decimal (or decimal approximation) for a fraction. Figure 6 shows how to find a decimal approximation for $\frac{1}{3}$ using a centiwheel. Point out to students that 0.33 is just an approximation since the line for $\frac{1}{3}$ lies between $\frac{33}{100}$ and $\frac{34}{100}$ on the wheel.

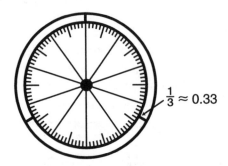

$\frac{1}{3} \approx 0.33$

Figure 6: *Decimal approximation for $\frac{1}{3}$ using a centiwheel*

Discuss repeating decimals *(Question 10).* To help illustrate that 0.333333333 is approximately equal to $\frac{1}{3}$, ask students to find the answer for $\frac{1}{3} \times 3$ on their calculator. (Enter $\boxed{1}$ $\boxed{\div}$ $\boxed{3}$ $\boxed{\times}$ $\boxed{3}$ $\boxed{=}$.) Students should note that the answer to this is 1. Then, ask students to find the answer to this problem by entering directly: $\boxed{0.333333333}$ $\boxed{\times}$ $\boxed{3}$ $\boxed{=}$. Students will note that this answer is 0.999999999. Explain that this is approximately one, but not exactly one.

Students can continue to work with their partners to complete *Questions 11–14.* They use calculators and centiwheels to find decimal equivalents or decimal approximations for fractions. Students are asked which of the decimals are decimal equivalents and which are approximations. If the decimal has repeating digits that fill the calculator display ($\frac{2}{3} = 0.666666667$), we can be fairly certain that the digits will continue to repeat and that the decimal in the display is an approximation. If the decimal terminates ($\frac{1}{8} = 0.125$), then we know that the decimal is equal to the fraction.

Questions 15–18 guide students toward a strategy for using calculators to see if two fractions are equivalent. They can use a calculator to find a decimal for each fraction. Then, if both decimals are equivalent, the fractions are equivalent. Point out *Question 17C* to students. Here $\frac{666}{1000} = 0.666$ which, although close to $\frac{2}{3}$, is not equivalent to $\frac{2}{3}$.

Suggestions for Teaching the Lesson

Homework and Practice

- Assign the *Dividing Pizzas* Homework Pages in the *Discovery Assignment Book* after completing **Question 4** (Part 1) in the *Student Guide.* Students should draw pictures when needed.

- Assign **Questions 1–5** in the Homework section of the *Student Guide* after the lesson is completed. Students will need a calculator and a small centiwheel to complete this work.

- Assign DPP items A–D for further practice with computation, elapsed time, and problem solving.

- Assign Part 1 of the Home Practice which practices division.

Answers for Part 1 of the Home Practice can be found in the Answer Key at the end of this lesson and at the end of this unit.

14. A. Use your calculator to change $\frac{3}{8}$ to a decimal. Write the decimal exactly as it appears on your calculator.
    B. Use your centiwheel and the fraction circle below to find a decimal for $\frac{3}{8}$ (to the nearest hundredth).
    C. Is $\frac{3}{8}$ exactly equal to or approximately equal to the decimal in Question 14A? How do you know?
    D. Is $\frac{3}{8}$ exactly equal to or approximately equal to the decimal in Question 14B? How do you know?

15. A. Use your calculator to find the decimal equivalent for $\frac{5}{8}$.
    B. Use your calculator to find the decimal equivalent for $\frac{10}{16}$.
    C. Is $\frac{5}{8} = \frac{10}{16}$? How do you know?
    D. Is $\frac{16}{20} = \frac{8}{9}$? Use your calculator to help you decide.
    E. How can you use your calculator to help you decide if two fractions are equivalent?

16. Use your calculator to help you decide which of the following fractions are equivalent to $\frac{3}{4}$.
    A. $\frac{15}{20}$ B. $\frac{8}{12}$
    C. $\frac{75}{100}$ D. $\frac{12}{16}$

17. Use your calculator to help you decide which fractions are equivalent to $\frac{2}{3}$.
    A. $\frac{6}{9}$ B. $\frac{7}{11}$
    C. $\frac{666}{1000}$ D. $\frac{44}{66}$

18. Use your calculator to help you decide which fractions are equivalent to $\frac{7}{8}$.
    A. $\frac{140}{160}$ B. $\frac{87}{100}$
    C. $\frac{875}{1000}$ D. $\frac{22}{25}$

Fractions and Division

Student Guide - Page 292

Daily Practice and Problems:
Task and Challenge for Lesson 1

B. Task: Arrival Time (URG p. 10)

Los Angeles is in the Pacific Standard Time (PST) zone and New York is in the Eastern Standard Time (EST) zone. When it is noon in Los Angeles, it is 3:00 P.M. in New York.

A plane left New York at 8:30 A.M. and took 5 hours to fly to Los Angeles. The time in Los Angeles is always 3 hours earlier than New York. What time will the plane arrive in Los Angeles?

D. Challenge: Arranging Colors (URG p. 11)

Lee Yah received three different-colored sweatshirts for her birthday—blue, red, and yellow. She is deciding which one to wear to school on Monday, Tuesday, and Wednesday.

1. In what order can she wear the three sweatshirts? List all the different ways.

2. If Lee Yah decides to wear the blue sweatshirt on Monday, in what order can she wear the other two shirts? List all the possibilities.

3. If she chooses not to wear the blue and yellow sweatshirts in a row (not blue, yellow and not yellow, blue), in what order could she wear the three sweatshirts? List all the different ways.

Homework

You will need a calculator and a small centiwheel to complete the homework.

1. A. Use your calculator to change $\frac{5}{12}$ to a decimal. Write the decimal exactly as it appears on your calculator.
   B. Use your centiwheel and the fraction circle divided into twelfths to find a decimal for $\frac{5}{12}$ (to the nearest hundredth).
   C. Is $\frac{5}{12}$ exactly equal to or approximately equal to the decimals in Question 1A and 1B? How do you know?

2. A. Use your calculator to change $\frac{8}{12}$ to a decimal. Write the decimal exactly as it appears on your calculator.
   B. Use your centiwheel and the fraction circle above to find a decimal for $\frac{8}{12}$ (to the nearest hundredth).
   C. Is $\frac{8}{12}$ equal to or approximately equal to the decimals in Question 2A and 2B? How do you know?

3. Use your calculator to help you decide which of the following fractions are equivalent to $\frac{2}{9}$.
   A. $\frac{6}{27}$ B. $\frac{10}{49}$ C. $\frac{5}{18}$ D. $\frac{22}{99}$

4. Use your calculator to help you decide which of the following fractions are equivalent to $\frac{15}{6}$.
   A. $\frac{12}{5}$ B. $\frac{76}{32}$ C. $2\frac{1}{2}$ D. $\frac{25}{10}$

5. Change each fraction to a decimal. Try different strategies and tools including calculators, centiwheels, or paper and pencil. Be prepared to share your strategies. Round decimals to the nearest hundredth when appropriate.
   A. $\frac{1}{5}$ B. $\frac{6}{8}$ C. $\frac{7}{10}$
   D. $\frac{7}{9}$ E. $\frac{7}{100}$

Fractions and Division

Student Guide - Page 293

Suggestions for Teaching the Lesson (continued)

Assessment

The homework activities can be used as assessments. Select specific questions to evaluate students' work. *Question 3* on the *Dividing Pizzas* Homework Pages in the *Discovery Assignment Book* can be used to assess students' abilities to see patterns with fractions. Homework *Questions 2–4* in the *Student Guide* can assess students' abilities to change fractions to decimal fractions for comparison.

Literature Connection

Little House in the Big Woods, by Laura Ingalls Wilder, Scholastic, New York, 1992. In Chapter 10, "Summertime," Ma lets Laura and Mary go to visit Mrs. Peterson. Mrs. Peterson gives each girl 1 cookie. They decide to save some for Baby Carrie, so they each eat $\frac{1}{2}$ of their cookie. When they get home, they realize that with their 2 halves, Baby Carrie gets a whole cookie. While they know that this is not quite fair, they can't decide how to divide the two cookies equally among the three children.

After reading this selection to your class, suggest that your students use rectangles or circles to decide how to divide the two cookies evenly among the 3 girls.

AT A GLANCE

Math Facts and Daily Practice and Problems

DPP items A–D review division, elapsed time, and problem solving.

Part 1. Fractions and Division

1. Read and discuss the vignette in the *Student Guide.*
2. Use *Questions 1–4* to connect fractions and division.

Part 2. Decimals

1. Use *Questions 5–8* to show students how to use calculators to find decimal equivalents for fractions.
2. Students work in pairs to change fractions to decimals using calculators. *(Question 9)*
3. Students use calculators and centiwheels to find approximations for repeating decimals and equivalents for terminating decimals. *(Questions 10–14)*
4. Students learn to use calculators to compare fractions to see if they are equivalent. *(Questions 15–18)*

Homework

1. Assign the *Dividing Pizzas* Homework Pages in the *Discovery Assignment Book* after Part 1 of the lesson.
2. Assign the Homework section in the *Student Guide.*
3. Assign Part 1 of the Home Practice.

Assessment

Use some of the questions on the homework pages as assessments. *Question 3* on the *Dividing Pizzas* Homework Pages and *Questions 2–4* in the *Student Guide* Homework section are good choices.

Notes:

Student Guide

Questions 1–18 (SG pp. 286–292)

1. **A.** 2; See Figure 1 in Lesson Guide 1.
    B. $\frac{2}{3}$
2. **A.** *See Figure 2 in Lesson Guide 1.
    B. 2
    C. $\frac{2}{4} = \frac{1}{2}$
    D. *See Figure 3 in Lesson Guide 1.
3. **A.** *$\frac{2}{5}$
    B. $\frac{2}{5} = 2 \div 5$
4. **A.** *$\frac{6}{4} = 1\frac{2}{4} = 1\frac{1}{2}$
    B. *See Figure 4 in Lesson Guide 1.
    C. $\frac{3}{2}$ and any number equivalent to $\frac{3}{2}$
5. *$\frac{1}{2}$
6. **A.** *See Figure 5 in Lesson Guide 1.
    B. $\frac{4}{5}$
    C. 0.8; $\frac{8}{10}$ and any number equivalent to $\frac{4}{5}$
    D. $0.8 = \frac{4}{5}$
7. **A.** *$\frac{1}{4}$
    B. *0.25
    C. $\frac{25}{100}$ and any number equivalent to $\frac{1}{4}$
8. **A.** *$\frac{1}{8}$
    B. *0.125
    C. $\frac{125}{1000}$ and any number equivalent to 0.125
    D. $\frac{1}{8} = \frac{125}{1000}$

9. Answers will depend on calculator.

Fraction	Decimal
$\frac{1}{10}$	0.1
$\frac{1}{8}$	0.125
$\frac{1}{4}$	.25
$\frac{1}{3}$	0.3333333
$\frac{2}{4}$	0.5
$\frac{1}{2}$	0.5
$\frac{2}{3}$	0.6666667
$\frac{3}{4}$	0.75
1	1.0
$\frac{9}{8}$	1.125
$\frac{5}{4}$	1.25
$\frac{14}{10}$	1.4

10. **A.** It has a repeating digit, 3.
    B. No; $\frac{1}{3} \approx 0.3333333$
    C. 0.33; *See Figure 6 in Lesson Guide 1.
11. **A.** 6
    B. Many calculators will show a 7.
    C. $\frac{2}{3} \approx 0.6666667$
    D.

$\frac{2}{3} \approx 0.67$

---

*Answers and/or discussion are included in the Lesson Guide.
**Answers for all the Home Practice in the *Discovery Assignment Book* are at the end of the unit.

12. **A.** 0.1666667 (Many calculators will show 0.1666667.)

B.

$\frac{1}{6} \approx 0.17$

C. approximately equal; The decimal has a repeating digit, 6.

13. **A.** 0.6

B.

$\frac{3}{5} = 0.60$

C. Equal; There is no repeating digit, and the decimal terminates after 6.

14. **A.** 0.375

B.

$\frac{3}{8} \approx 0.38$

C. Equal; The decimal terminates after 5 and there is no repeating digit.

D. Approximately equal; 0.375 is rounded to the nearest hundredth to get 0.38.

15. **A.** 0.625

B. 0.625

C. Yes; The decimal equivalent of each fraction is the same.

D. No; The decimal equivalent of each fraction is not the same.

E. Find the decimal equivalent of each fraction. If both decimals are equivalent, the fractions are equivalent.

16. $\frac{15}{20}, \frac{75}{100}, \frac{12}{16}$

17. *$\frac{6}{9}, \frac{44}{66}$

18. **A.** $\frac{140}{160}$ and **C.** $\frac{875}{1000}$

Homework (SG p. 293)

Questions 1–5

1. **A.** Many calculators will show 0.4166667.

B.

$\frac{5}{12} \approx 0.42$

C. Approximately equal; There is a repeating digit, 6.

2. **A.** 0.75

B.

$\frac{9}{12} = 0.75$

C. Equal; The decimal terminates after 5 and there is no repeating digit.

3. $\frac{6}{27}, \frac{22}{99}$

4. $2\frac{1}{2}, \frac{25}{10}$

5. **A.** 0.2

B. 0.75

C. 0.7

D. 0.78

E. 0.07

---

*Answers and/or discussion are included in the Lesson Guide.

**Answers for all the Home Practice in the *Discovery Assignment Book* are at the end of the unit.

Discovery Assignment Book

**Home Practice (DAB p. 147)

Part 1. Division Practice

Questions A–D

A. 720 R2   Possible strategy:
$5762 \div 8 \approx 5600 \div 8$ or 700

B. 140 R3

C. 1563 R2

D. 1063

Dividing Pizzas (DAB pp. 151–152)

Questions 1–4

1. A. $\frac{1}{4}$ B. $1 \div 4 = \frac{1}{4}$

2. A. $\frac{3}{4}$ B. $3 \div 4 = \frac{3}{4}$

3.

Sharing Pizzas

Number of Pizzas	Number of People	Number of Pizzas Each Person Will Get	Division Number Sentence
4	1	$\frac{4 \text{ pizzas}}{1 \text{ person}}$ = 4 pizzas per person	$4 \div 1 = 4$
4	2	$\frac{4 \text{ pizzas}}{2 \text{ people}}$ = 2 pizzas per person	$4 \div 2 = 2$
4	3	$\frac{4 \text{ pizzas}}{3 \text{ people}}$ = $\frac{4}{3} = 1\frac{1}{3}$ pizzas per person	$4 \div 3 = \frac{4}{3} = 1\frac{1}{3}$
4	4	$\frac{4 \text{ pizzas}}{4 \text{ people}}$ = 1 pizza per person	$4 \div 4 = 1$
4	5	$\frac{4 \text{ pizzas}}{5 \text{ people}}$ = $\frac{4}{5}$ pizzas per person	$4 \div 5 = \frac{4}{5}$
4	10	$\frac{4 \text{ pizzas}}{10 \text{ people}}$ = $\frac{4}{10}$ pizzas per person	$4 \div 10 = \frac{4}{10}$
4	20	$\frac{4 \text{ pizzas}}{20 \text{ people}}$ = $\frac{4}{20}$ pizzas per person	$4 \div 20 = \frac{4}{20}$

4. As the number of people increases, the amount of pizza per person will become smaller.

*Answers and/or discussion are included in the Lesson Guide.

**Answers for all the Home Practice in the *Discovery Assignment Book* are at the end of the unit.

LESSON GUIDE

Division

Estimated Class Sessions: 3

Students review the forgiving method for division. They solve division problems with two-digit divisors using this paper-and-pencil method. Estimation strategies for choosing partial quotients are emphasized.

Key Content

- Dividing with 2-digit divisors using paper and pencil.
- Checking division using *Quotient × Divisor + Remainder = Dividend.*
- Using estimation to choose more accurate numbers in the partial quotients.
- Estimating quotients.

Key Vocabulary

dividend
divisor
quotient
remainder

Daily Practice and Problems: Bits for Lesson 2

E. Estimating with Ease (URG p. 12)

See if you can figure out these problems in your head. Then, write down your reasoning for each answer.

1. About how many 12s are in 140?

2. About how many 25s are in 370?

3. About how many 20s are in 345?

G. Practicing the Facts
(URG p. 13)

A. $300 \div 50 =$ B. $400 \div 4 =$

C. $150 \div 3 =$ D. $100 \div 10 =$

E. $45 \div 5 =$ F. $2500 \div 5 =$

G. $600 \div 100 =$ H. $35 \div 7 =$

I. $10 \div 5 =$

I. Fractions, Decimals, and the Calculator
(URG p. 14)

Use a calculator to change each of the following fractions to decimals. Then, compare the decimals to see if each pair of fractions are equivalent.

A. $\frac{4}{7}$ and $\frac{3}{5}$ B. $\frac{1}{3}$ and $\frac{13}{39}$

C. $\frac{12}{15}$ and $\frac{8}{11}$

DPP Task and Challenges are on page 41. Suggestions for using the DPPs are on page 41.

Curriculum Sequence

Before This Unit

Students reviewed the forgiving method with one-digit divisors in Unit 4 Lesson 3. Interpreting remainders was also discussed.

After This Unit

Division practice will be included in the Daily Practice and Problems and Home Practice in all succeeding units.

Materials List

Print Materials for Students

	Math Facts and Daily Practice and Problems	Activity	Homework
Student Books			
Student Guide		*Division* Pages 294–298	*Division* Homework Section Page 298
Discovery Assignment Book		*Estimation and Division* Page 153 and *More Estimation and Division* Page 155	Home Practice Part 2 Page 147
Teacher Resources			
Facts Resource Guide	DPP Item 9G		
Unit Resource Guide	DPP Items E–J Pages 12–15		

available on Teacher Resource CD

All Transparency Masters, Blackline Masters, and Assessment Blackline Masters in the Unit Resource Guide are on the Teacher Resource CD.

Supplies for Each Student

base-ten pieces, optional

Materials for the Teacher

Introducing Division Transparency Master (Unit Resource Guide) Page 43, optional

Before the Activity

Use DPP item E to start the lesson on the first day. This item gives students practice using multiples of ten to estimate quotients.

Developing the Activity

Part 1. Introducing Division

Use the problems on the *Introducing Division* transparency to begin this lesson. When you display the transparency, cover all but the statement of the first problem. This problem is a review of the forgiving method. Ask:

- *What does each of the numbers in this problem stand for?* (96 is the number of students attending the play. 8 is the number of seats in each row or the number of students that can sit in each row.)

- *Copy the problem* 8 $\overline{)96}$ *onto a piece of paper and find the answer using the forgiving method. Explain your strategies for choosing the partial quotients.* (Possible responses: guessing, using multiplication facts, e.g., $8 \times 5 = 40$, $8 \times 9 = 72$, $8 \times 11 = 88$, or using multiples of 10, $8 \times 10 = 80$.)

Discuss the efficiency of the strategies they choose. Point out that choosing partial quotients that bring us closer to the final quotient and choosing numbers that lend themselves to mental computation are often more efficient. Complete the problem on the transparency using one or more of the suggested strategies as shown in Figure 7.

Figure 7: *Three possible paths for solving 96 ÷ 8*

TIMS Tip

If students have learned a different paper-and-pencil division method that they are proficient with, they should be allowed to use it to solve problems. However, we recommend that they still work through the questions with the forgiving method. Answering questions about the forgiving method will improve their understanding of the division process.

Content Note

Vocabulary Review. In the division problem 8 $\overline{)96}$, 8 is the **divisor** (the number you are dividing by) and 96 is the **dividend** (the number to be divided). The answer to a division problem is called the **quotient.**

TIMS Tip

Remind students of how they solved division problems with the base-ten pieces in Unit 4. In this problem you would need to distribute 9 skinnies and 6 bits into 8 groups (the rows). If needed, demonstrate the problem with the base-ten pieces or have students complete the problem with the base-ten pieces.

Ask:

- *What information does the quotient give us in this problem?* (12 rows are needed and they will be completely filled.)
- *How can you check your work?* (Since multiplication and division are related, you can check division by multiplying the quotient by the divisor and adding the remainder.)

Emphasize that **(quotient × divisor) + remainder = dividend.** Ask a student to check the division for the first problem on the transparency: $8 \times 12 = 96$. In this problem the remainder is 0 (or we can say no remainder).

Use the second problem on the transparency to introduce two-digit divisors. Stress estimations. Begin by asking:

- *Will the quotient have one, two, or three digits in it?* (Since $10 \times 24 = 240$ and $100 \times 24 = 2400$, guide students to see that the quotient will have two digits because 852 is between 240 and 2400.)

Once students understand that the quotient is between 10 and 99, ask:

- *Estimate a reasonable partial quotient.*

If students are having difficulty with this, suggest using multiples of 10 as one strategy. Using this strategy, 10, 20, or 30 would be reasonable partial quotients to start with. If a student estimates 40 as a partial quotient, show them that this estimate would be too large since $40 \times 24 = 960$.

Other strategies for finding a partial quotient are possible. For example, a student may suggest that there are at least thirty-two 24s in 852 since they know that 24 is almost 25 and there are four 25s in every 100. Encourage students to look at many different estimation strategies and to choose a strategy that is the most comfortable and the most efficient for them to use.

Start the problem using one of the partial quotients suggested by a student. One possible starting point is shown in Figure 8. Remind them that the 480 means that 480 apples have been taken care of (boxed) and 372 remain to be boxed.

$$
\begin{array}{r}
24 \overline{\smash{)}\,852} \\
-480 \quad | \, 20 \\
\hline
372
\end{array}
$$

Figure 8: *One possible partial quotient*

Ask students to estimate how many more boxes you need for the remaining apples. Depending on the first partial quotient used, students might use multiples of 10 again, or they may need to use a number smaller than 10. Continue finding partial quotients until the problem is complete. Once all the partial quotients have been found, students should add them together to find the solution to the problem (the quotient). Three possible solution paths are shown in Figure 9.

```
      35 R12            35 R12              35 R12
  24 | 852          24 | 852            24 | 852
    - 480    20       - 720    30         - 240    10
     372              132                 612
    - 240    10      - 120     5         - 240    10
     132               12     35          372
    - 120     5                          - 240    10
      12     35                           132
                                         - 120     5
                                           12     35
```

Figure 9: *Three possible paths for solving 852 ÷ 24*

Discuss:

• *Use multiplication to check the division.* (See Figure 10.)

• *What does the quotient mean?* (There are 35 complete boxes of apples with 12 apples remaining.)

```
     35          840
   × 24         + 12
     20          852
    120
    100
    600
    840
```

Figure 10: *Using multiplication to check a division problem*

After completing the transparency, students begin the *Division* Activity Pages in the *Student Guide.* In this lesson, students continue working with two-digit divisors. Read the short vignette together. Have students answer the questions in pairs before discussing them as a class.

Student Guide - Page 294

"This sounds like a division problem," said Manny. "To figure out the number of pans we need to prepare, we need to divide the total number of people we expect by the number of servings each pan will make."

$$32\overline{)389}$$

Discuss

"I know how to do this," Brandon exclaimed. "First we need to decide how many groups of 32 there are in 389. I think a good way to do this is to estimate with multiples of 10."

I. A. If Mr. Cline prepares 10 pans of enchilada casserole, how many people can the fifth grade serve?

B. Are 10 pans too much or too little?

C. How many people can they serve if Mr. Cline prepares 20 pans of enchilada casserole?

D. Are 20 pans too much or too little?

Brandon decided to start the division problem by estimating that they would need at least 10 pans of enchilada casserole. He recorded his work.

$$\begin{array}{r} 32\overline{)389} \\ -320 \quad | \quad 10 \\ \hline 69 \end{array}$$

E. If Mr. Cline made only 10 pans of casserole, how many people would not get served?

F. How did Brandon record this?

Student Guide - Page 295

"I think that we will need to make at least two more pans of enchilada casserole in order to feed everyone," said Arti. Arti recorded her work.

$$\begin{array}{r} 12 \text{ R5} \\ 32\overline{)389} \\ -320 \quad | \quad 10 \\ \hline 69 \\ -64 \quad | \quad \underline{2} \\ \hline 5 \quad | \quad 12 \end{array}$$

2. A. If Mr. Cline makes two more pans of casserole, how many more people can be served?

B. How many people will not be served?

"This shows that we need to make 10 + 2 or 12 pans of enchilada casserole to serve 320 + 64 or 384 people," said Manny. "We still have 5 people who will be without food. 5 is the remainder. Since we don't want anyone to be without food, Mr. Cline needs to make 1 more pan of casserole or a total of 13 pans."

Arti remembered that she could check her division by multiplying the **quotient** by the **divisor** and adding the **remainder**: $12 \times 32 + 5 = 389$. Arti's computation gave her the **dividend** 389, so she knew her division was correct.

Ordering Clay

The art teacher at Ontario School, Mrs. Sorenson, is ordering clay for the school.

Clay comes in 24-pound blocks. She knows that each student uses an average of 1 pound of clay each year. This year there are 531 art students. Mrs. Sorenson knows that she needs to divide 531 by 24 to find out how many blocks of clay she needs to order.

$$24\overline{)531}$$

3. A. What does the number 24 tell us in this problem?

B. What does the number 531 tell us in this problem?

Student Guide - Page 296

In *Question 1,* students use multiples of 10 to estimate the number of pans of casserole that will be needed. If 10 pans are prepared, students will be able to serve 320 people, and if 20 pans are prepared they will be able to serve 640 people. Since they are only expecting 389 people, 10 is a better estimate—preparing 20 pans would be too much food. Discuss how Brandon records his work using the forgiving method *(Questions 1E–1F).* The 320 tells the number of people who will be served if 10 pans of enchilada casserole are prepared; 69 shows the number of people who still need to be taken care of.

In *Question 2,* Arti estimates that they will need to make at least two more pans of enchilada casserole. Discuss her recorded work.

Discuss:

• *Why does Manny think they should make 13 pans of enchilada casserole instead of 12 pans?* (If 2 more pans were made, 64 more people could be served but 5 still do not get any casserole. 5 is the **remainder.**)

Question 3 leads students through a second division problem. For *Questions 3A–3B,* students tell what the numbers in this problem represent. The number 24 can be either the pounds of clay or the number of students for each block of clay. The number 531 is the number of art students in the school.

Mrs. Sorenson uses multiples of 25 to estimate her answer. In *Question 3C,* Mrs. Sorenson starts to find an exact answer. She records her work showing that 20 blocks will provide clay for 480 students; however, 51 students will not get clay unless she orders more blocks. In *Question 3D,* Mrs. Sorenson estimates she will need at least 2 more blocks of clay. Since her work shows that 3 students still remain without clay, Mrs. Sorenson needs to order 23 blocks of clay *(Question 3F).*

Part 2. Dividing with Larger Dividends

Once you have completed *Questions 1–3* in the *Student Guide,* ask:

• *What numbers might you use to estimate the quotient in the problem 8656 ÷ 42?* (Students should suggest using multiples of 100 to estimate.)

• *What multiple of 100 would be a good estimate to start with?*

Have students check their estimates using mental math as they did in **Question 1.** Students might think: 42 × 100 = 4200; 42 × 200 = 8400; 42 × 300 = 12,600. Good estimates are either 100 or 200. The most efficient estimate is 200. Record this and then complete the problem by using further estimations. One possible solution is shown in Figure 11.

Figure 11: *One path for completing this division problem using the forgiving method*

Part 3. Practicing Estimation

To give students more practice using estimation to begin division, assign the *Estimation and Division* Activity Page in the *Discovery Assignment Book.* Solve a problem from this page in class together before asking students to complete the remaining problems independently or in groups. Emphasize that students need only find an estimate. Good estimates will make efficient partial products when they begin a division problem.

Assign the *More Estimation and Division* page for homework. Remind students to find efficient estimates and to explain their strategies.

Part 4. Practicing Division

Students can work on **Questions 4–7** in the Explore section of the *Student Guide* independently or with a partner. One strategy that is often successful is to have students complete the work independently and then meet with a partner to compare their work. Both partners should be able to explain and justify the steps that they took to reach their answers.

Remind students to interpret the remainders carefully. For example, **Question 4A** asks how many tables are needed to seat 389 people if 12 people can sit at one table. Since 389 ÷ 12 = 32 R5, 33 tables are needed to seat all 389 people.

Students should choose efficient strategies to solve each problem. For example, for **Question 7D** students can reason that there are two 50s in one hundred and eighteen 50s in 900.

Since 24 is close to 25 and Mrs. Sorenson knows that there are four 25s in 100, she decides to use multiples of 25 to estimate how many blocks of clay she should order. Mrs. Sorenson estimates that she should order at least 20 blocks of clay, since there are twenty 25s in 500.

    C. If she orders only 20 blocks of clay, how many students will not get clay this year?

    D. Mrs. Sorenson sees that she needs to order at least two more blocks of clay. She records her second estimate. Is this enough clay to make sure that each student will get clay? Explain your answer.

    E. Write a number sentence to check the division.

    F. How much clay should Mrs. Sorenson order so that every child will get clay? Explain your answer.

Complete the following problems. Use estimation to help you divide. Record your work using a paper-and-pencil method. Write a number sentence to check your work.

  4. The students at Bessie Coleman School are setting up tables for their parent dinner. Students can use either the rectangular tables or the round tables.

    A. Each of the rectangular tables will seat 12 people. How many rectangular tables will they need to seat all 389 people?

    B. Each of the round tables will seat 10 people. How many round tables will they need to seat all 389 people?

  5. Alexis, Edward, and Irma are making centerpieces for each table. Each centerpiece will use 24 inches of ribbon. They have a spool with 864 inches of ribbon.

    A. How many centerpieces can they make?

    B. Will they have enough centerpieces to place one on each of the rectangular tables if they use only rectangular tables? Explain your answer.

    C. Will they have enough centerpieces to place one on each of the round tables if they use only round tables? Explain your answer.

Student Guide - Page 297

Name _____ Date _____

Estimation and Division

Estimate each quotient. Tell what strategy you used to make your estimate.

Example: 22 $\overline{)834}$

Think:

22 × 10 =	220
22 × 20 =	440
22 × 30 =	660
22 × 40 =	880

←834

Answer: I used multiples of 10. Since 834 is between 22 × 30 = 660 and 22 × 40 = 880, the quotient will be at least 30 but less than 40.

  1. 11 $\overline{)258}$ 2. 21 $\overline{)753}$

  3. 32 $\overline{)568}$ 4. 25 $\overline{)648}$

  5. 42 $\overline{)3253}$ 6. 38 $\overline{)6206}$

  7. 50 $\overline{)792}$ 8. 73 $\overline{)7890}$

Discovery Assignment Book - Page 153

6. The plates that the students will use come in packages of 48.
   A. How many packages will they need to serve all 389 people?
   B. How many plates will be left over?

7. A. $39\overline{)873}$ B. $12\overline{)3706}$
   C. $26\overline{)785}$ D. $50\overline{)900}$

Homework

For Problems 1–6:

A. Use a paper-and-pencil method or mental math to solve each division problem. Record all your work on your paper.

B. Check your answer using a different method. Write a number sentence to show how you checked your work.

1. $20\overline{)163}$ 2. $36\overline{)952}$ 3. $40\overline{)8000}$

4. $56\overline{)598}$ 5. $45\overline{)3607}$ 6. $23\overline{)4594}$

7. Jackie has chosen a book from the library that has 364 pages. She wants to finish reading it in two weeks. How many pages should she plan to read each day?

8. Mr. Moreno asked Edward and Roberto to help him divide 943 marbles evenly among 15 bags.
   A. How many marbles will be in each bag?
   B. Will there be any marbles left over? If so, how many?

9. Mr. Moreno wanted to know the average number of miles he traveled each day. He kept track of the miles he traveled and found that in a two-week period he traveled 882 miles. What is the average number of miles he traveled each day?

10. Mr. Cline is making rolls for the school lunch. He needs 465 rolls. Each package contains 12 rolls. How many packages should he prepare?

11. Mrs. Sorenson is cutting ribbon for an art project. She has 650 cm of ribbon. Each student needs a strip 15 cm long. How many strips can she cut?

Student Guide - Page 298

Homework *Questions 1–11* provide practice using a paper-and-pencil method for division. Encourage students to use estimation as they work through each step of these problems. They will check their work in *Questions 1–6* using multiplication. *Questions 7–11* provide an opportunity for students to use division to solve problems. They need to think about the remainders in these problems to answer the questions.

Journal Prompt

If you were planning a party and you needed to purchase party favors, plates, cups, and napkins, how can division help you plan how much you need to buy? Give examples to help explain your thoughts.

Name _____   Date _____

More Estimation and Division

Estimate each quotient. Tell what strategy you used to make your estimate.

Example: $27\overline{)8432}$

Think:

25 × 200 =	5000
25 × 300 =	7500
25 × 400 =	10,000

←— 8432

Possible answer: Use 25 as a convenient number for 27. I tried multiples of 100. Since 8432 is between 25 × 300 and 25 × 400, the quotient is between 300 and 400.

1. $12\overline{)497}$ 2. $79\overline{)9898}$

3. $52\overline{)6449}$ 4. $26\overline{)8970}$

5. $17\overline{)874}$ 6. $32\overline{)9583}$

Discovery Assignment Book - Page 155

Suggestions for Teaching the Lesson

Math Facts

DPP item G practices the division facts for the 5s and 10s.

Homework and Practice

- DPP Bit E provides practice estimating quotients.

- The *More Estimation and Division* Activity Page in the *Discovery Assignment Book* can be assigned as homework after Part 3 of the lesson.

- Use DPP items F, H, I, and J to review concepts including fractions, decimals, problem solving, and division.

- Assign homework *Questions 1–11* in the *Student Guide* after completing Part 4 of the lesson.

- Assign Part 2 of the Home Practice which reviews fractions and decimals.

Answers for Part 2 of the Home Practice can be found in the Answer Key at the end of this lesson and at the end of this unit.

Assessment

Use the Homework section in the *Student Guide* to assess students' understanding of a paper-and-pencil method to compute division problems.

Name _____ Date _____

Unit 9: Home Practice

Part 1 Division Practice

Solve each problem using paper and pencil. Estimate to see if your answers are reasonable. Explain your estimation strategy for Question A.

A. $5762 \div 8 =$ B. $1263 \div 9 =$

C. $4691 \div 3 =$ D. $3189 \div 3 =$

Part 2 Fractions and Decimals

1. Find a pair of equivalent fractions in each set. You may use a calculator or another strategy. Be prepared to explain your thinking.

A. $\frac{7}{15}$ $\frac{28}{75}$ $\frac{79}{160}$ $\frac{21}{45}$

B. $\frac{15}{20}$ $\frac{125}{200}$ $\frac{3}{5}$ $\frac{27}{45}$

C. $\frac{1}{3}$ $\frac{33}{100}$ $\frac{4}{5}$ $\frac{11}{33}$

D. $\frac{6}{16}$ $\frac{24}{36}$ $\frac{36}{112}$ $\frac{66}{176}$

2. Use your calculator to change each fraction to a decimal (to the nearest hundredth). Then, change each decimal to a percent.

	Decimal	Percent
A. $\frac{4}{5}$	_____	_____
B. $\frac{7}{12}$	_____	_____
C. $\frac{4}{15}$	_____	_____

CONNECTIONS TO DIVISION   DAB · Grade 5 · Unit 9   **147**

Discovery Assignment Book - Page 147

Daily Practice and Problems: Task & Challenges for Lesson 2

F. Challenge: Tenths, Hundredths, and Thousandths (URG p. 13)

1. Name a decimal that is greater than 0.3 but less than 0.35.

2. Name a decimal that is greater than 0.25 but less than 0.26.

3. Name a decimal that is greater than 0.403 but less than 0.41.

4. Name a fraction that is greater than $\frac{57}{100}$ but less than $\frac{7}{10}$.

5. Name a fraction that is greater than $\frac{8}{16}$ but less than 0.8.

6. Name a fraction that is greater than 17% but less than 0.2.

H. Challenge: Craft Fair
(URG p. 14)

1. Lee Yah and Manny are setting up tables for the fifth-grade family craft show. Each table is 200 cm long. Tables will line up along two sides of the room which measure 12 meters each. Each participant who wishes to sell crafts pays a $15 rental fee for one table or $25 for two tables. Mr. Moreno tells the students that all the tables have been rented. Only 2 people rented two tables. How much money will the school make on the craft show?

2. The community craft show will be held in the gym next month. The school is charging $25 for one table and will have five times as many tables as the fifth-grade craft show. How much will the school make for hosting the community craft show if all of the tables are rented?

J. Task: Division Practice (URG p. 15)

Use estimation to help you divide. Use a paper-and-pencil method or mental math. Show how you check your work.

A. $23\overline{)756}$ B. $20\overline{)4000}$

C. $42\overline{)8973}$ D. $75\overline{)684}$

AT A GLANCE

Math Facts and Daily Practice and Problems

DPP item G practices the division facts for the 5s and 10s. Items E, F, H, I, and J review concepts including area, decimals, problem solving, fractions, and estimation.

Before the Activity

Use Bit E to begin the lesson. It provides practice with estimating quotients.

Part 1. Introducing Division

1. Use the problems on the *Introducing Division* transparency in the *Unit Resource Guide* to review the forgiving method for division.
2. Read the vignette on the *Division* Activity Pages in the *Student Guide*. Discuss **Question 1**. Encourage students to use multiples of 10 as a strategy to estimate the quotient.
3. Discuss the remainder and how it is used in **Question 2.**
4. Discuss the strategy of using multiples of 25 to estimate. **(Question 3)**

Part 2. Dividing with Larger Dividends

Complete the problem $8656 \div 42$ using multiples of 100 to estimate the quotient.

Part 3. Practicing Estimation

Assign the *Estimation and Division* Activity Page in the *Discovery Assignment Book*.

Part 4. Practicing Division

Students answer **Questions 4–7** on the *Division* Activity Pages in the *Student Guide.*

Homework

1. Assign the *More Estimation and Division* Activity Page in the *Discovery Assignment Book.*
2. Assign the Homework section in the *Student Guide.*
3. Assign Part 2 of the Home Practice.
4. Assign DPP Task J.

Assessment

The Homework section of the *Student Guide* can be used as an assessment.

Notes:

Introducing Division

1. Ninety-six students from Bessie Coleman Elementary School are attending a play at a local theater. They will sit in rows of 8 seats. How many rows will they need to seat all the students? Will each row be completely filled?

$$8 \overline{)96}$$

2. There are 852 apples that need to be packaged into boxes of 24 apples. How many boxes will you need?

$$24 \overline{)852}$$

Student Guide

Questions 1–7 (SG pp. 295–298)

1. **A.** *320
   B. Too little
   C. 640
   D. Too much
   E. 69
   F. Using the forgiving method. He still has 69 to take care of.

2. **A.** 64
   B. 5

3. **A.** *The number 24 can be either the pounds of clay or the number of students for each block of clay.
   B. *The number 531 is the number of art students in the school.
   C. *51 students
   D. *No; There will still be 3 students who will not get any clay.
   E. $22 \times 24 + 3 = 531$
   F. 23 pounds; Since she doesn't want any students without clay, she needs to order one more pound in addition to the 22 pounds.

4. **A.** *33 tables

   $$
   \begin{array}{r}
   32R5 \\
   12\overline{)389} \\
   -360 \quad 30 \\
   \hline
   29 \\
   -24 \quad 2 \\
   \hline
   5 \quad 32
   \end{array}
   $$
   $32 \times 12 + 5 = 389$

   B. 39 tables

   $$
   \begin{array}{r}
   38R9 \\
   10\overline{)389} \\
   -300 \quad 30 \\
   \hline
   89 \\
   -80 \quad 8 \\
   \hline
   9 \quad 38
   \end{array}
   $$
   $38 \times 10 + 9 = 389$

5. **A.** 36
   B. Yes; There are only 33 rectangular tables. Each table can have a centerpiece and there will be 3 centerpieces left over.
   C. No; There are 39 round tables and only 36 centerpieces.

6. **A.** 9 packages
   B. 43 plates

7. **A.** 22 R15; $22 \times 39 + 15 = 873$
   B. 308 R10; $308 \times 12 + 10 = 3706$
   C. 30 R5; $30 \times 26 + 5 = 785$
   D. *18; $18 \times 50 = 900$

Homework (SG p. 298)

Questions 1–11

For *Questions 1–6,* estimates will vary.

1. $20 \times 8 + 3 = 163$

   $$
   \begin{array}{r}
   8R3 \\
   20\overline{)163} \\
   -100 \quad 5 \\
   \hline
   63 \\
   -60 \quad 3 \\
   \hline
   3 \quad 8
   \end{array}
   $$

2. $26 \times 36 + 16 = 952$

   $$
   \begin{array}{r}
   26R16 \\
   36\overline{)952} \\
   -720 \quad 20 \\
   \hline
   232 \\
   -144 \quad 4 \\
   \hline
   88 \\
   72 \quad 2 \\
   \hline
   16 \quad 26
   \end{array}
   $$

3. $8000 \div 40 = 200$
   $40 \times 200 = 8000$

4. $10 \times 56 + 38 = 598$

   $$
   \begin{array}{r}
   10R38 \\
   56\overline{)598} \\
   -560 \quad 10 \\
   \hline
   38 \quad 10
   \end{array}
   $$

*Answers and/or discussion are included in the Lesson Guide.
**Answers for all the Home Practice in the *Discovery Assignment Book* are at the end of the unit.

5. $80 \times 45 + 7 = 3607$

```
        80R7
45 | 3607 |
   -2700 | 60
    907 |
   - 900 | 20
      7 | 80
```

6. $199 \times 23 + 17 = 4594$

```
       199R17
23 | 4594 |
   -2300 | 100
    2294 |
   -1150 | 50
    1144 |
   - 920 | 40
    224 |
   - 115 | 5
    109 |
   -  92 | 4
     17 | 199
```

7. 26 pages

8. **A.** 62 marbles

   B. Yes; 13 marbles will be left over.

9. 63 miles

10. 39 packages

11. 43 strips

Discovery Assignment Book

**Home Practice (DAB p. 147)

Part 2. Fractions and Decimals

Questions 1–2

1. **A.** $\frac{7}{15} = \frac{21}{45}$ **B.** $\frac{3}{5} = \frac{27}{45}$
   C. $\frac{1}{3} = \frac{11}{33}$ **D.** $\frac{6}{16} = \frac{66}{176}$

2. **A.** 0.8, 80%   **B.** 0.58, 58%
   C. 0.27, 27%

Estimation and Division (DAB p. 153)

Questions 1–8

For *Questions 1–8* answers and strategies will vary.

1. Between 20 and 30.
2. Between 30 and 40.
3. Between 10 and 20.
4. Between 20 and 30.
5. Between 50 and 100.
6. Between 100 and 200.
7. Between 10 and 20.
8. Between 100 and 200.

More Estimation and Division (DAB p. 155)

Questions 1–6

For *Questions 1–6* answers and strategies may vary.

1. Between 40 and 50.
2. Between 100 and 130.
3. Between 100 and 130.
4. Between 300 and 400.
5. Between 50 and 60.
6. Between 250 and 320.

*Answers and/or discussion are included in the Lesson Guide.

**Answers for all the Home Practice in the *Discovery Assignment Book* are at the end of the unit.

OPTIONAL LESSON

LESSON GUIDE 3

Multiplication Methods

Estimated Class Sessions: 2

Different methods for paper-and-pencil multiplication are discussed in the context of checking a division problem. Lattice multiplication is introduced. Students solve problems involving two-digit by three-digit multiplication.

Key Content

- Introducing lattice multiplication.
- Multiplying 2 digits × 3 digits using paper-and-pencil methods.
- Comparing multiplication methods.

Key Vocabulary

lattice multiplication

Curriculum Sequence

Before This Unit

In Unit 2, students explored two methods of paper-and-pencil multiplication—the all-partials method and the compact method. Egyptian multiplication was described in the fourth grade Adventure Book *Phil and Howard's Excellent Egyptian Adventure* in Unit 11.

Materials List

Print Materials for Students

	Optional Activity	Homework
Student Guide	*Multiplication Methods* Pages 299–303	*Multiplication Methods* Homework Section Page 303
Discovery Assignment Book	*Lattice Multiplication Practice* Pages 157–158	

(○) available on Teacher Resource CD

All Transparency Masters, Blackline Masters, and Assessment Blackline Masters in the Unit Resource Guide are on the Teacher Resource CD.

Developing the Activity

Part 1. Multiplying with Pencil and Paper

This lesson discusses several multiplication algorithms. Use the *Multiplication Methods* Activity Pages in the *Student Guide* to guide discussion. Mr. Moreno's class discusses two paper-and-pencil multiplication methods for checking whether $9568 \div 26 = 368$. Ask students to solve 26×368 with pencil and paper and look for the strategies they devise to solve the problem. If they recall their work with the all-partials method in Unit 2, they may use the strategy shown in the *Student Guide*.

There are a great many strategies that students can use. For example, one common strategy is to think of twenty-six as $10 + 10 + 6$, twenty-six 368's is $10 \times 368 + 10 \times 368 + 6 \times 368$. So, the result is:

$$10 \times 368 = 3680$$
$$10 \times 368 = 3680$$
$$6 \times 368 = 2208$$
$$\text{since } 3680 + 3680 + 2208 = 9568$$
$$\text{then } 26 \times 368 = 9568$$

In *Questions 3–8,* students discuss the all-partials method as a way to compute 26×368. Previously, students used the all-partials method to multiply two-digit by two-digit and one-digit by multidigit problems. Multiplying two-digit by three-digit numbers is a natural extension. Some students may be familiar with the traditional compact method of multiplying:

$$
\begin{array}{r}
1\,1 \\
4\,4 \\
368 \\
\times\ 26 \\
\hline
2208 \\
7360 \\
\hline
9568
\end{array}
$$

Multiplication Methods

Multiplying with Pencil and Paper

Mr. Moreno's class decided to make a book of the best short stories that they wrote. They decided to call this book "Life in Fifth Grade." Mr. Moreno made copies of the book on the school copy machine. He used 9568 sheets of paper. He knows that he used 26 sheets of paper to make each book.

1. How many copies of "Life in Fifth Grade" did Mr. Moreno make?

2. Ana divided the 9568 sheets of paper by 26 and got the answer 368 copies. Is Ana correct? Show how you would check Ana's answer.

Multiplication Methods   SG · Grade 5 · Unit 9 · Lesson 3   299

Student Guide - Page 299

Romesh checked Ana's calculation by multiplying. He used the all-partials method to multiply 26 by 368.

$$
\begin{array}{r}
368 \\
\times\ 26 \\
\hline
48 \\
360 \\
1800 \\
160 \\
1200 \\
6000 \\
\hline
9568
\end{array}
$$

3. How did Romesh get the partial product 48?
4. How did Romesh get the partial product 1200?
5. How did Romesh get the partial product 6000?
6. What color is the ones' column shaded?
7. What color is the tens' column shaded?
8. Which column is shaded green and which column is shaded yellow?

Lattice Multiplication

Blanca said she knew another way to multiply 368×26. She called it **lattice multiplication**. To start the problem she drew this diagram with 368 across the top and 26 down the right side.

300 SG · Grade 5 · Unit 9 · Lesson 3   **Multiplication Methods**

Student Guide - Page 300

She multiplied 8 × 2 and filled in 16.

Blanca then filled in all the partial products in the lattice, like this:

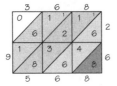

Finally, she added the columns along the diagonal. If a column totaled more than 9, she "carried" a digit to the next column to the left. This is what the problem looked like when she was done.

Student Guide - Page 301

Compare Blanca's method with Romesh's method. The diagonals have been colored to help you think about this.

9. Where do you see the answer to 26 × 368 in Blanca's method?

10. Compare the digits shaded orange in Blanca's method to the digits shaded orange in Romesh's method. What is similar?

11. Compare the digits shaded blue in Blanca's method to the digits shaded blue in Romesh's method. What is similar?

12. What color are the thousands shaded in both methods?

"The lattice is like a place value chart. The diagonals have different place values," said Blanca.

Student Guide - Page 302

Part 2. Lattice Multiplication

In the Lattice Multiplication section of the *Multiplication Methods* Activity Pages, Blanca introduces another paper-and-pencil multiplication method. **Lattice multiplication** is really a variation of the all-partials method. The lattice method arranges the partial products in such a way that you do not have to write down the ending zeros. Putting the products in the lattice automatically puts the digits in the correct place value columns. Many students enjoy using this method.

The *Student Guide* shows one example of lattice multiplication, a two-digit times a three-digit number. The same method can be extended to work for any multiplication problem.

To solve 26 × 368, follow these steps.

Step 1: Draw a 2 by 3 lattice and put the factors across the top and right hand side.

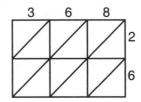

Step 2: Multiply the first partial product and fill it in.

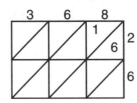

$8 \times 2 = 16$

Step 3: Fill in each of the partial products as shown. For example, $8 \times 6 = 48$, so 48 is entered in the lower right hand corner.

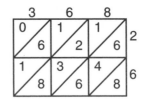

Step 4: Add the numbers along the diagonal columns. You have to "carry" if you have a sum greater than nine. The product, 9568, is displayed along the left hand and bottom sides of the lattice.

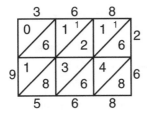

Encourage students to compare the all-partials method to lattice multiplication using *Questions 9–12* in the *Student Guide*.

Assign the *Lattice Multiplication Practice* Activity Pages in the *Discovery Assignment Book* for additional practice using lattice multiplication.

Part 3. Many Ways to Multiply

The Many Ways to Multiply section in the *Student Guide* points out that there are many different correct methods for multiplying numbers using pencil and paper. All the methods are based on the idea of breaking up the multiplication problem into groups and computing the groups individually, although this is not always so obvious. You may find that some students will come into your class having learned a different algorithm. If they have a method that works, that's fine, and they should continue using their method if it is efficient.

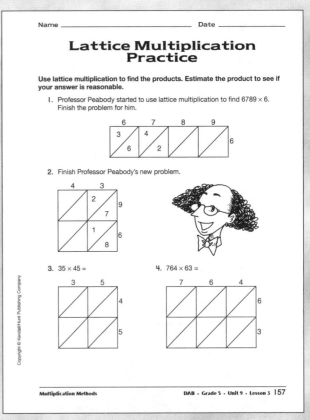

Discovery Assignment Book - Page 157

Discovery Assignment Book - Page 158

Content Note

We have refrained from emphasizing the traditional compact algorithm for two-digit by three-digit (and larger) problems, because it is hard to explain why it works and the time it would take to train students to do this method quickly and accurately would take away from time spent on understanding important concepts. If you feel it is necessary to teach students a multidigit algorithm that is more compact than the all-partials method, we suggest you teach them lattice multiplication.

Have students complete *Questions 13–16* in the *Student Guide* using two different multiplication algorithms of their choice.

Journal Prompt

Compare all the methods that you have used for multiplication. Are some methods better than others? Why? Which method do you like the best?

The Journal Prompt asks students which methods they like the best and why. Encourage students to justify their choices and to explain their reasoning, showing examples on the blackboard or overhead. Discuss when it is appropriate to use a calculator and estimation. Calculators are appropriate when speed and accuracy are important. Estimation is appropriate when an exact answer is not necessary or not meaningful. For more background on the *Math Trailblazers* approach to computation and journal writing, see the TIMS Tutor: *Arithmetic* and the TIMS Tutor: *Journals* in the *Teacher Implementation Guide*.

Suggestions for Teaching the Lesson

Homework and Practice

- Assign the *Lattice Multiplication Practice* Activity Pages in the *Discovery Assignment Book* for additional practice.

- Assign the Homework section in the *Student Guide*.

Assessment

While knowledge of multiplication facts is absolutely essential, there is no need to drill students for speed in using the multiplication algorithm. In any situation where speed is necessary, i.e., where numerous exact answers are required, the technology to solve these problems (namely, calculators and computers) is available. Therefore, we recommend that you avoid assessments containing many multi-digit multiplication problems that assess speed of computation. A moderate number of problems in which students can use any paper-and-pencil method is more appropriate.

Many Ways to Multiply

Jessie, Blanca, Romesh, Roberto, and Arti worked on the problem 37 × 499. They each used a different method.

"I didn't realize there were so many methods for multiplying," said Romesh.

"Yes," said Jessie. "I learned the compact method from my Dad."

"There are a lot more methods than the ones we have talked about. In some countries children learn even different methods," replied Mr. Moreno. "Most methods are based on the idea that multiplication problems with big numbers can be broken into many multiplications."

Find the following products in at least two different ways. Discuss with your classmates which methods were most efficient. Which were most reliable?

13. 36 × 502   14. 499 × 6

15. 53 × 123   16. 76 × 804

Homework

Estimate the answers to the following problems. Then, show how to find an exact answer using as many methods as you can.

1. 4598 × 5   2. 45 × 36

3. 201 × 35   4. 399 × 32

5. 3002 × 50

6. Which method of solving these problems do you like the most? Do you think the same method is best for all problems?

Multiplication Methods   SG · Grade 5 · Unit 9 · Lesson 3   303

Student Guide - Page 303

AT A GLANCE

Part 1. Multiplying with Pencil and Paper

1. Students solve 26 × 368 using their own strategies.
2. Read the Multiplying with Pencil and Paper section of the *Multiplication Methods* Activity Pages in the *Student Guide.*
3. Students complete *Questions 1–8.*

Part 2. Lattice Multiplication

1. Show students how to do 26 × 368 using lattice multiplication.
2. Read and discuss the Lattice Multiplication section in the *Student Guide.* Compare the all-partials method and lattice multiplication by looking at which digits appear in each place value column. *(Questions 9–12)*
3. Students complete the *Lattice Multiplication Practice* Activity Pages in the *Discovery Assignment Book.*

Part 3. Many Ways to Multiply

1. Read together the Many Ways to Multiply section in the *Student Guide.*
2. Students solve the multiplication problems in *Questions 13–16* using at least two methods.
3. Students compare all the methods that they use for multiplication by writing a response to the journal prompt.

Homework

1. Assign the *Lattice Multiplication Practice* Activity Pages.
2. Assign the Homework section in the *Student Guide.*

Notes:

Student Guide

Questions 1–16 (SG pp. 299–303)

1. 368

2. Yes; $368 \times 26 = 9568$

3. 6×8

4. 60×20

5. 300×20

6. Orange

7. Blue

8. Hundreds' column is colored green and thousands' column is colored yellow.

9. Left hand side and bottom of lattice

10. In both methods the digit shaded orange or the ones' digit is the same, 8.

11. In both methods the digits shaded blue or the tens' digits are the same, 4, 6, and 6.

12. Yellow

For *Questions 13–16* methods will vary.

13. 18,072

14. 2994

15. 6519

16. 61,104

Homework (SG p. 303)

Questions 1–6

For *Questions 1–5,* answers may vary. One possible estimate is given for each question.

1. 25,000; 22,990

2. 2000; 1620

3. 7000; 7035

4. 12,000; 12,768

5. 150,000; 150,100

6. Answers will vary.

Discovery Assignment Book

Lattice Multiplication Practice (DAB pp. 157–158)

Questions 1–8

1. Answer: 40,734

2. Answer: 4128

3. Answer: 1575

4. Answer: 48,132

5. Answer: 2212

6. Answer: 54,321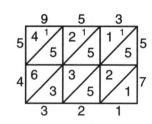

7. Answers will vary. The problem must be a 2-digit by 2-digit multiplication problem.

8. Answers will vary. The problem must be a 3-digit by 2-digit multiplication problem.

*Answers and/or discussion are included in the Lesson Guide.

**Answers for all the Home Practice in the *Discovery Assignment Book* are at the end of the unit.

LESSON GUIDE

Understanding Remainders

Estimated
Class
Sessions:
2

Students interpret remainders in division problems. They complete problems in which a remainder requires rounding the quotient to the next whole number, the remainder is dropped from the answer, and the remainder is the answer to the problem. Students also express quotients as mixed numbers.

Key Content

- Interpreting remainders in division problems.
- Writing quotients as mixed numbers.
- Solving division problems.

Daily Practice and Problems:
Bits for Lesson 4

K. More Fact Practice (URG p. 15)

Find *n* to make each number sentence true.

A. $n \times 5 = 40$ B. $n \times 7 = 70$

C. $n \div 4 = 5$ D. $80 \div n = 10$

E. $10 \times n = 50$ F. $30 \div 5 = n$

G. $9 \times 10 = n$ H. $15 \div n = 5$

I. $n \times 8 = 80$

M. Multiplying and Dividing
    by Multiples of Ten (URG p. 16)

A. $80 \times 500 =$ B. $60 \times 100 =$

C. $20 \times 5000 =$ D. $3000 \div 60 =$

E. $70{,}000 \div 100 =$ F. $4500 \div 90 =$

DPP Tasks are on page 58. Suggestions for using the DPPs are on page 58.

Curriculum Sequence

Before This Unit

Students explored remainders to division problems in Lessons 2 and 3 of Unit 4. They worked with mixed numbers and equivalent fractions in Units 3 and 5.

Materials List

Print Materials for Students

	Math Facts and Daily Practice and Problems	Activity	Homework	Written Assessment
Student Books				
Student Guide		*Understanding Remainders* Pages 304–308	*Understanding Remainders* Homework Section Pages 308–309	
Discovery Assignment Book			Home Practice Parts 3 & 4 Pages 148–149	
Teacher Resources				
Facts Resource Guide ◎	DPP Items 9K and 9M			
Unit Resource Guide	DPP Items K–N Pages 15–17 ◎			DPP Item N, *Operations,* Page 17 ◎ *Tie Dye T-Shirts* Page 60, 1 per student

◎ *available on Teacher Resource CD*

All Transparency Masters, Blackline Masters, and Assessment Blackline Masters in the Unit Resource Guide are on the Teacher Resource CD.

Developing the Activity

Part 1. Understanding Remainders

Review the *Division* Activity Pages in the *Student Guide* for Lesson 2. In this vignette, some students from Mr. Moreno's class are helping to plan a menu for a parent dinner. They decide how many pans of enchilada casserole will be needed by dividing the expected number of people by the number of servings each pan will make. Looking at just the paper-and-pencil computation, students see that the quotient is 12 with a remainder of 5. Ask:

- *How does the remainder in this problem help you decide how many pans of casserole are needed?* (The remainder shows that if they make 12 pans of enchilada casserole, five people will not get any food. As a result, the children must make one more pan of casserole.)

Ask students to open their *Student Guides* to the *Understanding Remainders* Activity Pages. *Questions 1–3* can be completed in small groups followed by an opportunity to share and discuss answers in the large group. For each of these questions, students compute the answer using paper and pencil.

In *Question 1,* students decide how many buses will be needed to transport a group of children to weekend camp. One way of completing the paper-and-pencil computation using the forgiving method is shown in Figure 12.

$$
\begin{array}{r}
5 \text{ R43} \\
63 \overline{\smash{)}\,358} \\
-315 \quad\Big|\;5 \\
\hline
43
\end{array}
$$

Figure 12: *A paper-and-pencil computation for* **Question 1**

In this problem, the remainder tells the number of students that will not have a seat on the bus if only 5 buses are used. Having a remainder greater than zero tells us that 1 more bus is needed, for a total of 6 buses.

In *Question 2,* students are asked how many tents can be set up if there are 102 tent stakes and each tent uses 8 stakes. The quotient 12 and remainder 6 tells us that after we set up 12 tents we will still have 6 stakes left over. Since 6 stakes are not enough for another tent, the remainder is dropped from the answer. Only 12 tents can be set up.

Understanding Remainders

Discuss

The remainder in a division problem is used in different ways, depending on the problem that you are solving.

1. There are 358 children going on a weekend camping trip. The children will ride buses to the camp. Each bus seats 63 children. How many buses are needed?
   A. Write a division problem for this question. Use paper and pencil to find an answer.
   B. What does the remainder mean in this problem?
   C. How did you use the remainder to decide how many buses are needed?

2. Some of the children want to sleep in tents. They need 8 stakes to set up each tent. They have 102 stakes. How many tents can they set up?
   A. Write a division problem for this question. Use paper and pencil to find an answer.
   B. What does the remainder mean in this problem?
   C. How did you use the remainder to decide how many tents can be set up?

3. The camp cook has 1282 cookies to divide into boxes. Each cabin will receive one box of cookies. There are 30 cabins in all. The cook promised all of the leftover cookies to the camp office staff get to share?
   A. Write a division problem for this question. Use paper and pencil to find an answer.
   B. What does the remainder mean in this problem?

Understanding Remainders

Student Guide - Page 304

C. How should you use the remainder to decide how many cookies the camp office staff will get to share?
D. If there are 4 members of the camp office staff, how many cookies will each person get?

Explore

Solve each of the following problems using paper and pencil. Explain how the remainder is used in each answer.

4. The Ontario School is hosting a sports day. Mrs. Sorenson is making medals for awards. Each medal uses 18 inches of ribbon. Mrs. Sorenson has 1450 inches of ribbon. How many medals can she make?

5. Award certificates come in packages of 25. Mrs. Lange, the principal, plans to give a certificate to each student in an event. There are 962 children competing in the events. How many packages of certificates should be ordered?

6. A. There are 92 children playing volleyball. Teams of 6 players are preferred but teams of 7 will be accepted. How many teams can be formed?
   B. How many teams will have a seventh player?
   C. How can you use multiplication to check your answer?

7. A. Jessie's mom is baking oatmeal bars for the refreshment table. She bought 4 dozen eggs. She already had 5 eggs at home. She uses 3 eggs for each pan she makes. How many pans can she make?
   B. After making the bars, Jessie's mom decided to bake a cake. The recipe calls for 4 eggs. Can she bake the cake using the leftover eggs?

8. The 160 fifth graders made teams for soccer of 11 players each. The extra students will be officials. How many students will be officials?

Understanding Remainders

Student Guide - Page 305

9. **A.** At the end of the sports day, 1697 ice cream treats were served to the children and their families. The treats came in boxes of 36. How many boxes of ice cream treats were opened?

   B. The leftover ice cream treats were given to the volunteers. How many ice cream treats did they get to share?

More Remainders

The answer to a division problem can be written as a whole number and a remainder or as a mixed number. A mixed number is a whole number plus a fraction. Depending on the problem, one way may be more useful than another.

Lin and David have 18 graham crackers to split among 8 children. To find out how many graham crackers to give each child, Lin wrote this problem: $\frac{18}{8}$ and David wrote this problem: $8\overline{)18}$

10. How are these two problems the same?

Lin found that $\frac{18}{8}$ equals $2\frac{2}{8}$ or $2\frac{1}{4}$. Each child will receive 2 whole crackers. The two leftover crackers will be divided into 8 equal pieces.

Lin's Solution

When David solved his problem, he found that 18 divided by 8 is 2 with a remainder of 2 crackers. He wrote his answer as a mixed number: $2\frac{2}{8}$. The fraction $\frac{2}{8}$ in the mixed number $2\frac{2}{8}$ shows that he took the two crackers that were left over and divided them among the eight children.

$$8\overline{)18} \quad \begin{array}{r} 2\ R2 \\ \hline 18 \\ -16 \\ \hline 2 \end{array} \quad 2 \quad 2\frac{2}{8}$$

David's Solution

11. **A.** Where did David get the numbers in this fraction?
    B. What information does the numerator give in this fraction?
    C. What information does the denominator give in this fraction?
    D. Rename $\frac{2}{8}$ using smaller numbers in the numerator and denominator.

Student Guide - Page 306

E. How many crackers will each child receive?

Explore

12. Mrs. Sorenson has large rolls of paper for bulletin boards and murals. She has 690 yards. There are 24 classrooms in the school. If she divides the paper evenly among the 24 classrooms, how many yards of paper can each class use this year?

Mrs. Sorenson used the forgiving division method. She found that each class can use 28 yards of paper, but she will still have a remainder of 18 yards. Mrs. Sorenson wants to divide this 18 yards among the 24 classes.

$$\begin{array}{r} 28\ R18 \\ 24\overline{)690} \\ -480 \quad 20 \\ \hline 210 \\ -192 \quad 8 \\ \hline 18 \quad 28 \end{array}$$

   A. What fraction should Mrs. Sorenson write to show 18 divided among 24 classes?

   B. What is another name for this fraction using smaller numbers?

   C. How much more paper can she give to each classroom?

   D. What is the total amount of paper that each classroom can use?

13. Mr. Moreno filled his gas tank before leaving on a weekend trip. He drove 351 miles before stopping to refill his tank. When he refilled his gas tank, he found that he had used 15 gallons of gas. What is the average number of miles Mr. Moreno traveled on each gallon of gas? Write the answer as a mixed number.

Student Guide - Page 307

Question 3 asks students to decide how many cookies of the 1282 cookies made will be given to the camp staff to share. These cookies are the leftovers after the cook has tried to distribute the cookies evenly among 30 cabins of children. Once students divide the cookies among the 30 boxes, they will see that there are 22 cookies left. Since the camp staff is to receive the leftover cookies, the remainder becomes the answer. **Question 3D** asks students to divide the 22 leftover cookies among 4 members of the camp staff. Some students may answer that each camp staffer will receive 5 cookies with 2 cookies left over, others may answer that each camp staffer will receive $5\frac{1}{2}$ cookies (dividing the remainder using fractions). Both responses are acceptable, but students should justify their responses.

If students understand how to use remainders, assign **Questions 4–9** to be completed independently in class or at home. If students need further guided practice, students can complete these questions in small groups.

Part 2. More Remainders

This section introduces students to quotients written as mixed numbers. Read the More Remainders section of the *Understanding Remainders* Activity Pages in the *Student Guide*. Students read and discuss the problem of dividing the graham crackers. In **Question 10**, $\frac{18}{8}$ and $8\overline{)18}$ are compared. These represent two ways to write 18 divided by 8. Remind students that a fraction is another way to write division, as discussed in Lesson 1. Discuss the diagram in the *Student Guide* showing Lin's solution.

Look at David's solution. Read through the steps that David took in order to find his solution.

Question 11A asks students why David wrote his quotient as a mixed number. Help students to see that the numerator represents the remainder, while the denominator represents the divisor. In **Questions 11B–11C,** students are asked the meaning of the numerator and denominator. The numerator in this fraction tells students the number of leftover crackers. The denominator in this fraction tells students the number of children the crackers are to be divided among.

Question 11D asks students to rename $\frac{2}{8}$. While there are many ways to rename this fraction, we ask them to rename using smaller numbers. Thus their answer should be $\frac{1}{4}$ (i.e., they have simplified or reduced the fraction). After answering *Question 11E,* students should see that each child will receive $2\frac{1}{4}$ crackers using both Lin's method of dividing and David's method of dividing.

For *Question 12* students should read and discuss the steps that Mrs. Sorenson takes as she computes 690 divided by 24 using the forgiving method. For *Question 12A,* students express 18 divided by 24 as a fraction. Make sure students understand that the 18 is the numerator and 24 is the denominator: $\frac{18}{24}$. This fraction is renamed as $\frac{3}{4}$ in *Question 12B.* In *Question 12C,* this fraction is interpreted to mean that each classroom can have an additional $\frac{3}{4}$ of a yard of paper. In *Question 12D,* students find that each classroom will receive $28\frac{3}{4}$ yards of paper this year.

Questions 13–15 provide additional practice with quotients expressed as mixed numbers. Students may work in small groups or independently. Provide opportunities for students to discuss their answers and receive feedback. *Question 15* asks students to find the number of bricks needed for each row in a walkway. To complete this problem, students will need to express the length of each row in inches. You may need to help students see that 8 feet 6 inches equals $8 \times 12 + 6$ or 102 inches.

Journal Prompt

Why are remainders important in a division problem? What information can they give you about your answer? Give examples.

---

14. The Simply Shirts Company used 608 yards of fabric to make 64 shirts. How much fabric is used in each shirt? Write the answer as a mixed number.

15. Nila is helping her father lay a walkway. They will lay bricks in rows that are each 8 feet 6 inches long. Each brick is 8 inches long. How many bricks will they need for each row in the walkway? Write the answer as a mixed number.

Homework

For each of the problems write the answer as a mixed number.

1. Frank and his mother made wooden trains to sell at the yearly craft sale. Over a two-month period they worked a total of 63 hours and made 18 trains. How many hours did it take to make each train?

2. On a pizza day at Bessie Coleman School, 78 pizzas were divided equally among 24 classrooms. How much pizza did each class receive?

3. The TIMS Candy Company made 60 pounds of Chocos. They put these candies in 24 gift boxes. How many pounds of candy are in each gift box?

4. Romesh is helping his mother build a fence. The fence will be 62 feet 3 inches long. Each fence board is 6 inches wide. How many boards will they need?

5. A. $12\overline{)507}$ B. $22\overline{)825}$
   C. $30\overline{)1800}$ D. $24\overline{)1260}$

Student Guide - Page 308

Solve each of the problems in Questions 6–10 using paper and pencil.

6. Jackie is working at Billy's Fruit Stand after school. Jackie has to put 2600 apples into bags. Each bag holds three dozen apples. How many bags can she fill?

7. Mrs. Colligan is buying enough lemons so that her third grade class can sell lemonade during lunchtime. The recipe they will use calls for 8 lemons for a pitcher of lemonade. Each pitcher serves 10 people.
   A. If they plan to make enough lemonade to serve 480 students and teachers, how many pitchers do they have to make?
   B. Eighteen lemons come in a bag. How many bags of lemons should she buy?

8. Billy divides 60 pounds of cherries evenly into 24 boxes. How many pounds of cherries are in each box?

9. Jackie's last job for the day is to divide 725 oranges evenly and put them into 45 bags. Billy told her that she may take any extras home. How many oranges can Jackie take home?

Write any remainders in Question 10 as whole numbers.

10. A. $41\overline{)8945}$ B. $60\overline{)4800}$ C. $68\overline{)4912}$

Student Guide - Page 309

Daily Practice and Problems: Tasks for Lesson 4

L. Task: *Digits Game:* Addition with Decimals (URG p. 16)

Draw boxes like these on your paper.

$$\frac{\begin{array}{c}\square\,\square.\square \\ +\ \square.\square\,\square\end{array}}{}$$

As your teacher or classmate chooses digits from a deck of digit cards, place them in the boxes. Try to make the largest sum. Remember that each digit will be read only once. Once you place a digit, it cannot be moved.

N. Task: Operations (URG p. 17)

Use paper and pencil or mental math, not your calculator, to solve these problems. Write any remainders as whole numbers. When you finish a problem, look back to see if your answer is reasonable.

A. $59 \times 14 =$ B. $86 \times 42 =$

C. $409 \times 4 =$ D. $2486 \div 4 =$

E. $2486 \div 14 =$ F. $1067 \div 37 =$

Suggestions for Teaching the Lesson

Math Facts

DPP items K and M provide multiplication and division practice with the 5s and 10s.

Homework and Practice

- Use **Questions 4–9** from the *Understanding Remainders* Activity Pages as homework.
- Assign homework **Questions 1–10** in the *Student Guide*.
- Use DPP Task L to review adding decimals in a game format.
- Assign Parts 3 and 4 of the Home Practice. Part 3 reviews multiplication and division. Part 4 provides practice with interpreting remainders.

Answers for Parts 3 and 4 of the Home Practice can be found in the Answer Key at the end of this lesson and at the end of this unit.

Assessment

- Use the *Tie Dye T-Shirts* Assessment Page as an assessment.
- Use DPP Task N to assess students' multiplication and division skills.

Name _____ Date _____

Part 3 Multiplication and Division Practice
Solve the following problems using paper and pencil or mental math. Estimate each answer to be sure it is reasonable.

A. $63 \times 45 =$ B. $221 \div 6 =$ C. $35 \times 29 =$

D. $8406 \div 23 =$ E. $0.52 \times 0.5 =$ F. $918 \div 54 =$

G. $0.83 \times 27 =$ H. $4500 \div 15 =$ I. $12{,}744 \div 68 =$

Discovery Assignment Book - Page 148

Name _____ Date _____

Part 4 Using Remainders
Solve each of the problems below. Show how you solved each one. Be sure to label the numbers you use, especially your answers.

Four hundred seventy-eight students from Bessie Coleman School are going to the Lizardland Amusement Park for a day.

1. At the Lizardland Amusement Park the roller coaster has 15 cars. Each car holds 4 people. What is the least number of times it will have to run to give all 478 students a ride?

2. Hot pretzels come in packages of 24. The pretzel stand will prepare two pretzels for each student. The workers at the stand will eat the rest of the pretzels. How many will the workers get to eat?

3. The park workers are putting up banners to welcome the school. They use a whole roll of paper that is 200 feet long for the banners. If they make 16 signs, how long will each sign be?

4. The Lizardland train has cars that can carry 18 passengers. If 250 people are riding the train, how many cars will be full?

5. For each of the problems, write any remainder as a mixed number.
   A. $425 \div 15 =$ B. $3500 \div 50 =$ C. $4005 \div 18 =$

Discovery Assignment Book - Page 149

Copyright © Kendall/Hunt Publishing Company

AT A GLANCE

Math Facts and Daily Practice and Problems

DPP items K and M review the multiplication and division facts for the 5s and 10s. Items L and N review decimals, multiplication, and division.

Part 1. Understanding Remainders

1. Review the opening vignette on the *Division* Activity Pages in the *Student Guide* for Lesson 2.
2. Students complete *Questions 1–3* on the *Understanding Remainders* Activity Pages in the *Student Guide*.
3. Provide opportunities in class to discuss the strategies used in *Questions 1–3*.
4. Students complete *Questions 4–9* on the *Understanding Remainders* Activity Pages. These can be used as independent practice, small group work, or homework.

Part 2. More Remainders

1. Discuss *Questions 10–11* from the More Remainders section.
2. Introduce writing a quotient as a mixed number.
3. Students complete *Question 12* as additional guided practice.
4. Students complete *Questions 13–15*.

Homework

1. Assign *Questions 4–9* on the *Understanding Remainders* Activity Pages.
2. Assign homework *Questions 1–10* in the *Student Guide*.
3. Assign Parts 3 and 4 of the Home Practice.

Assessment

1. Students complete the *Tie Dye T-Shirts* Assessment Page.
2. Use DPP Task N as a quiz.

Notes:

Tie Dye T-Shirts

Solve the following problems using a paper-and-pencil method.

I. Mrs. Sorenson needs 384 white t-shirts to tie dye. If there are 12 t-shirts in a box, how many boxes of t-shirts should Mrs. Sorenson order?

2. Mrs. Sorenson got large bottles of dye from the dye factory. Each bottle will dye 18 t-shirts.

   A. How many bottles of dye should Mrs. Sorenson buy to dye all 384 t-shirts?

   B. If Mrs. Sorenson bought 19 bottles of dye, how many t-shirts would be left white?

Student Guide

Questions 1–15 (SG pp. 304–308)

1. 6 buses

   A. *$358 \div 63 = 5$ R43; See Figure 12 in Lesson Guide 4 for the paper-and-pencil method.

   B. The remainder tells the number of students that will not have a seat on the bus if only 5 buses are used.

   C. Since the remainder is greater than zero, there should be one more bus, for a total of 6 buses.

2. *12 tents

   A. $102 \div 8 = 12$ R6; Methods will vary.

   B. The remainder of 6 means that after setting up 12 tents, there will be 6 stakes left over.

   C. Since 6 stakes are not enough for another tent, the remainder is dropped and only 12 tents can be set up.

3. *22 cookies

   A. $1282 \div 30 = 42$ R22

   B. The remainder tells how many cookies are left over after dividing all the cookies evenly among the 30 cabins.

   C. The remainder is the number of cookies left over. Therefore, it is the number of cookies the camp office staff gets to share.

   D. *$5\frac{1}{2}$ cookies

4. 80 medals; The remainder 10 inches is not enough for another medal, and therefore, it is dropped.

5. 39 packages; After using 38 packages there will be 12 students left over. Since every student must receive a certificate, one more package should be ordered, for a total of 39 packages.

6. A. 15 teams

   B. 2 teams

   C. $13 \times 6 + 2 \times 7 = 92$

7. A. 17 pans

   B. No; There are only 2 eggs left over and she needs 4 eggs to bake the cake.

8. 6 students

9. A. 48 boxes

   B. 31 ice cream treats

10. *These are two different ways of writing the problem 18 divided by 8.

11. A. *The numerator represents the remainder, and the denominator represents the divisor.

    B. *The numerator tells the number of leftover crackers.

    C. *The denominator tells the number of children the crackers are to be divided among.

    D. *$\frac{1}{4}$

    E. $2\frac{1}{4}$

12. A. $\frac{18}{24}$ B. $\frac{3}{4}$

    C. $\frac{3}{4}$ yard   D. $28\frac{3}{4}$ yards

13. $23\frac{6}{15} = 23\frac{2}{5}$ miles

14. $9\frac{32}{64}$ or $9\frac{1}{2}$ yds

15. *$12\frac{6}{8} = 12\frac{3}{4}$ bricks

Homework (SG pp. 308–309)

Questions 1–10

1. $3\frac{1}{2}$ hours

2. $3\frac{1}{4}$ pizzas

3. $2\frac{1}{2}$ pounds

4. $124\frac{1}{2}$ boards

5. A. $42\frac{3}{12}$ or $42\frac{1}{4}$

   B. $37\frac{11}{22}$ or $37\frac{1}{2}$

   C. 60

   D. $52\frac{12}{24}$ or $52\frac{1}{2}$

6. 72 bags

7. A. 48 pitchers

   B. 22 bags

8. $2\frac{1}{2}$ lb

9. 5 oranges

10. A. 218 R7

    B. 80

    C. 72 R16

*Answers and/or discussion are included in the Lesson Guide.

**Answers for all the Home Practice in the *Discovery Assignment Book* are at the end of the unit.

Discovery Assignment Book

**Home Practice (DAB pp. 148–149)

Part 3. Multiplication and Division Practice

Questions A–I

A. 2835   B. 36 R5

C. 1015   D. 365 R11

E. 0.26   F. 17

G. 22.41   H. 300

I. 187 R28

Part 4. Using Remainders

Questions 1–5

1. 8 runs
2. 4 pretzels
3. 12.5 feet or $12\frac{1}{2}$ feet
4. 13 cars
5. A. $28\frac{5}{15}$ or $28\frac{1}{3}$
   B. 70
   C. $222\frac{9}{18}$ or $222\frac{1}{2}$

Unit Resource Guide

Tie Dye T-Shirts (URG p. 60)

Questions 1–2

1. 32 boxes

```
        32
   12 ) 384
      - 360  | 30
        24
      - 24   | 2
         0     32
```

2. A. 22 bottles   B. 42 t-shirts

*Answers and/or discussion are included in the Lesson Guide.

**Answers for all the Home Practice in the *Discovery Assignment Book* are at the end of the unit.

Calculator Strategies: Division

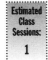

Estimated Class Sessions: 1

Students explore using a calculator to divide larger numbers and money. They develop strategies for finding whole number remainders using calculators.

Key Content

- Using a calculator to divide larger numbers.
- Using a calculator to divide money.
- Finding a whole number remainder using a calculator.
- Estimating quotients.

Daily Practice and Problems: Bit for Lesson 5

O. Estimate the Products (URG p. 17)

Estimate the products. Be prepared to share how you estimated.

A. $4.2 \times 53 =$ B. $0.63 \times 0.18 =$

C. $0.25 \times 119 =$ D. $19 \times 81.56 =$

E. $2.09 \times 3.982 =$ F. $66 \times 9.09 =$

DPP Task is on page 67. Suggestions for using the DPPs are on page 67.

Materials List

Print Materials for Students

		Math Facts and Daily Practice and Problems	Activity	Homework
Student Books	Student Guide		*Calculator Strategies: Division* Pages 310–312	*Calculator Strategies: Division* Homework Section Pages 312–313
	Discovery Assignment Book			Home Practice Part 5 Page 150
Teacher Resources	Unit Resource Guide	DPP Items O–P Pages 17–18 ◎		

◎ *available on Teacher Resource CD*

All Transparency Masters, Blackline Masters, and Assessment Blackline Masters in the Unit Resource Guide are on the Teacher Resource CD.

Supplies for Each Student

calculator

Calculator Strategies: Division

Think about this division problem: 29 ⟌ 42,601

1. A. Why is using a calculator a good method for finding the answer to this problem?
   B. Use estimation to decide if the quotient is in the 100s, the 1000s, or the 10,000s.
   C. Here is a set of keystrokes you can use on your calculator to find an answer to this division problem: [42601] [÷] [29] [=] . Use your calculator to solve this problem. Is your answer reasonable based on your estimate?

Money

2. The Parent Teacher Organization gave Mrs. Sorenson $1140 to share among the 24 classrooms for extra art supplies. First she used a paper-and-pencil method to divide the money. She found that she could give each classroom $47.00, but that would leave a remainder of $12.00.

```
        47 R12
   24 ⟌ 1140
      - 960    40
        180
      - 168    7
         12   47
```

Next, she used her calculator to divide the money among the classrooms.
   A. What keystrokes can she use to find an answer to this division problem?
   B. Use your calculator to decide how much money each classroom should receive.
   C. What do the numbers to the left of the decimal point mean?
   D. What do the numbers to the right of the decimal point mean?
   E. Why is a calculator a good tool for dividing money?

Calculator Strategies: Division

Student Guide - Page 310

Developing the Activity

When students divide larger numbers, they should use calculators to find the quotient. This is a more efficient method than paper-and-pencil procedures. Students need to practice using their calculators so that they are comfortable with the keystrokes. They also need to practice estimating to see if their answers are reasonable.

Content Note

For this lesson we assume that students are using calculators that have the correct order of operations, but do not necessarily have features that will display quotients with integer remainders or as mixed numbers. Work with students so that they take advantage of the features that their calculators offer, so they can solve problems as efficiently as possible.

Order of Operations on Calculators. See the Unit 4 Lesson 5 Lesson Guide for information on how to determine if a calculator has the correct order of operations. If your students do not have calculators with this feature, you will need to help them enter the steps in multistep calculations to get the correct answers.

Integer Division on Calculators. Some calculators include two choices for division. One set of keystrokes will produce a decimal. Another set of keystrokes will display a quotient with a whole number remainder.

Converting Decimals to Fractions. Some scientific calculators will change decimals to fractions. Students can use this feature to change decimal quotients to mixed numbers.

Ask students to turn to the *Calculator Strategies: Division* Activity Pages in their *Student Guides*. *Question 1* asks students why using a calculator is a good method for dividing these larger numbers. Students may respond with the following comments:

- It will save time.
- You save space on your paper when you use a calculator.
- It is quicker than using paper and pencil.

Ask students what problems might arise when using a calculator. Student responses might include:

- The calculator is only as accurate as the person using it. In other words, if you do not enter the correct keystrokes, your answer will not be correct.
- It is sometimes harder to interpret remainders.

In *Question 1B,* students estimate the size of the quotient for the problem 29 $\overline{)42{,}601}$. To estimate, students need to decide if the quotient will be in the 100s, 1000s, or 10,000s. It might be helpful to organize their thoughts using a chart as shown in Figure 13.

$29 \times 100 =$	2900
$29 \times 1000 =$	29,000
$29 \times 10{,}000 =$	290,000

Figure 13: *A chart for estimating the size of this quotient*

Since 42,601 is between 29,000 (29×1000) and 290,000 ($29 \times 10{,}000$) the quotient will be at least 1000 but less than 10,000. This means that the quotient will be in the 1000s.

Students are shown the keystrokes that they can use to divide 42,601 by 29. The keystrokes are shown in Figure 14. Make sure students understand that they key in the dividend first, in this case 42,601.

42,601	÷	29	=	1469

Figure 14: *Keystrokes for 42,601 ÷ 29 =*

After finding the solution to this problem using their calculators, students should confirm that the quotient, 1469, is between 1000 and 10,000.

Question 2 leads students through a problem of dividing money. Students compare a paper-and-pencil method with the calculator method. In *Question 2A,* students identify the keystrokes used to find the quotient using the calculator. The keystrokes are shown in Figure 15.

1140	÷	24	=	47.5

Figure 15: *Keystrokes for 1140 ÷ 24 =*

In *Question 2C,* students should identify the numbers to the left of the decimal point in the quotient as the number of dollars each class will receive.

In *Question 2D,* the numbers to the right of the decimal are identified as the number of cents each class will receive. Explain to students that the calculator displays 0.50 as 0.5. Make sure students do not interpret that as 5 cents. Remind them that 0.5 is half of a dollar and that 5 cents is 5 hundredths of a dollar or 0.05.

Use a calculator to solve these problems. List your keystrokes and tell what the numbers to the left and to the right of the decimal point mean.

3. A school spent $2489 to replace 76 science books. What was the cost of each book?

4. The Tasty Pizzeria served 52 large cheese pizzas in one evening. They calculated a total of $650 on the sale of these pizzas. How much did each pizza cost?

5. Three students earned a total of $5.00 washing cars. If they split the money evenly, how much will each student receive?

Whole Number Remainders

6. A. Jackie and Jessie are dividing cookies into boxes for a bake sale. They have 231 cookies and they are putting 12 into each box. Use your calculator to divide 231 by 12.

 B. What does the number to the left of the decimal point tell you?

 C. What does the number to the right of the decimal point tell you?

 D. Jessie and Jackie fill 19 boxes with cookies. How many cookies have they put in boxes?

To find the number of leftover cookies, Jackie first found 12 × 19 = 228. This means 228 cookies have been packed. To find the number of cookies remaining, Jackie computed 231 − 228 = 3 cookies.

Student Guide - Page 311

Use a calculator to solve these problems. Show your operations with number sentences and tell what the numbers to the left and to the right of the decimal point mean. Give whole number remainders with your answer.

7. The Happy Day Bakery made 542 muffins on Monday.
 A. If they package 2 dozen (24) muffins per box, how many full boxes of muffins did they package?
 B. How many muffins did not get packaged?

8. Penny and Pete's Pencil Company made 38,664 pencils. They packaged them in boxes of 144 pencils.
 A. How many full boxes can they package?
 B. How many pencils will be left over?

Homework

For Questions 1–4, estimate the size of each quotient. Use your calculator to find the answer to each division problem. Write each remainder as a whole number.

Example: $\dfrac{264.5 = 264\ R19}{38\ \overline{)10,051}}$

1. $44\ \overline{)23,375}$ 2. $52\ \overline{)150,000}$ 3. $39\ \overline{)164,754}$ 4. $15\ \overline{)8925}$

Use your calculator to solve the following problems. Write your remainder as a whole number.

5. David has collected 1385 different stamps. He wants to organize them in a book.
 A. If he puts 20 stamps on each page, how many full pages will he use?
 B. How many stamps will be left?

Student Guide - Page 312

In *Question 2E,* students identify the advantages of using a calculator to solve this problem. One advantage is that the calculator gives the remainder as a decimal and this decimal remainder can easily be read as cents, while the paper-and-pencil method gives the remainder as left over whole dollars.

Students practice solving more problems involving money in *Questions 3–5.* In *Question 5,* remind students to give their answer in dollars and cents. Note that 5 ÷ 3 = 1.6666667. Each student will get $1.66 and two cents will be left over.

In *Question 6,* students develop strategies for finding the whole number remainder when they divide using a calculator. In *Question 6A,* students use their calculators to divide 231 by 12. They should see 19.25 on their displays after completing the problem. For *Question 6B,* students tell what the number to the left of the decimal stands for in this problem. This number tells the number of boxes of cookies Jessie and Jackie can fill for the bake sale. The number to the right of the decimal point is the remainder. In this case, it tells you that you will have 0.25 of a box of cookies remaining *(Question 6C).* Discuss:

- *Suggest strategies for finding the number of cookies remaining.* (Remind students that they can multiply to check their answers to division problems.)

Three possible strategies:

1. Multiply 19 by 12 to find out how many cookies the girls used to fill the boxes: 19 × 12 = 228 cookies. Then, subtract to find how many cookies are left: 231 − 228 = 3 cookies. This number (3) is the whole number remainder.

2. Some students may also remember that .25 is equal to $\frac{1}{4}$. Since there are 12 cookies in a whole box, they can solve $\frac{1}{4}$ of 12 to find 3 as the whole number remainder.

3. Multiply 0.25 × 12 = 3.

Questions 7–8 provide additional practice using a calculator to divide. These problems can be assigned as independent or small group practice.

TIMS Tip

If students have calculators that will display whole number remainders, help them take advantage of this feature to solve problems more efficiently.

Suggestions for Teaching the Lesson

Homework and Practice

- *Questions 1–10* in the Homework section of *Calculator Strategies: Division* Activity Pages provide independent practice. Students will need a calculator to complete these problems. Remind students to check their calculators at home for the correct order of operations.

- DPP Bit O provides practice estimating the product of two decimals.

- Assign Part 5 of the Home Practice that includes multistep word problems that require interpretation of remainders.

Answers for Part 5 of the Home Practice can be found in the Answer Key at the end of this lesson and at the end of this unit.

Assessment

Homework *Questions 1 and 9* can be used to assess students' ability to use the calculator accurately to divide larger numbers and numbers involving money.

Extension

Practice subtraction with decimals in a game format using DPP item P. You will need *Digit Cards* from the Generic Section to play this game.

Name _____ **Date** _____

Part 5 Solving Problems

Choose an appropriate method to solve each of the following problems. For each question, you may choose to use paper and pencil, mental math, or a calculator. Use a separate sheet of paper to explain how you solved each problem. (*Hint:* Drawing a picture may help you solve some of the problems.)

1. Penny's Pencil Company donated a case of pencils to Bessie Coleman Elementary School. The case contains 48 packs of pencils. Each pack contains 24 pencils. The principal wants to divide the pencils equally among 30 classrooms. How many pencils will each classroom receive? How many pencils will be left over for the office?

2. Mr. Moreno is putting together blank research journals for the fifth grade. Each journal needs 7 sheets of paper. Mr. Moreno has 2 packages of paper to use for the journals. How many journals can he make if one package of paper has 144 sheets?

3. The school is sponsoring a cultural fair. The fifth graders are arranging tables and chairs for a refreshment area at the fair. Half of the tables will seat 8 people. Half of the tables will seat 6 people. They have 112 chairs. How many of each kind of table will they set up?

4. One of the classes is serving burritos at the cultural fair. They will use 3 ounces of cheese on each burrito. How many burritos can they make if they have 5 pounds of cheese? (1 pound = 16 ounces)

5. During the cultural fair a group of students will demonstrate an Irish dance. There are 130 chairs available for the audience. The chairs are arranged into 8 equal rows. How many chairs are in each row? How many extra chairs will there be?

6. A. At the end of the fair, one group of students found that they served 384 egg rolls. The egg rolls came in boxes of 18. How many boxes of egg rolls did they need?

   B. The extra egg rolls were given to the volunteers. How many egg rolls did the volunteers get to share?

   C. If each volunteer got the same number of egg rolls and there were 12 volunteers, how many egg rolls did each volunteer get?

7. A. Mr. Moreno took 78 pictures at the cultural fair. He wanted to arrange the pictures in an album. Each page of his album holds 8 pictures. How many pages of his album can he completely fill?

   B. How many pages will he have to use in all?

Copyright © Kendall/Hunt Publishing Company

150 **DAB** · Grade 5 · Unit 9   **CONNECTIONS TO DIVISION**

Discovery Assignment Book - Page 150

P. Task: *Digits Game:* Subtraction with Decimals (URG p. 18)

Draw boxes like these on your paper.

As your teacher or classmate chooses digits from a deck of digit cards, place them in the boxes. Try to make the largest difference. Remember that each digit will be read only once. Once you place a digit, it cannot be moved.

---

6. Irma is cutting ribbon for a craft project. Each piece must be 16 inches long. She has 508 inches of ribbon.
   A. How many 16-inch pieces can she cut?
   B. How many inches of ribbon will be left?

Use your calculator to solve these problems. Explain any remainders.

7. Mrs. Morgan is a civil engineer. Her job is to plan a bike path around the new park. She needs to decide how many lights she will need along the path. Mrs. Morgan knows that there must be a light every 120 feet. How many lights will she need if the path is 12 miles long? (*Hint:* There are 5280 feet in 1 mile.)

8. Crystal Clear window washers washed some large windows on a skyscraper for $3500. If they washed 56 windows on the skyscraper, how much did the company charge to wash each window?

9. Perky's Plentiful Peanuts purchased 28 pounds of peanuts from a proprietor for $46.76. How much did Perky's Plentiful Peanuts pay per pound of peanuts?

10. Perky's Plentiful Peanuts puts 24 peanuts in a package. Pat, the packer, packaged 1375 peanuts. She ate the leftover peanuts. How many peanuts did she eat?

Calculator Strategies: Division   SG · Grade 5 · Unit 9 · Lesson 5   313

Student Guide - Page 313

AT A GLANCE

Math Facts and Daily Practice and Problems

DPP items O–P review estimation and subtraction with decimals.

Developing the Activity

1. Use *Question 1* on the *Calculator Strategies: Division* Activity Pages to begin a discussion about calculator use.
2. Review strategies for estimating the size of a quotient.
3. Students use calculators to divide large numbers involving money and discuss remainders. *(Questions 2–5)*
4. Students develop strategies for finding whole number remainders using calculators. *(Questions 6–8)*

Homework

1. Assign homework *Questions 1–10* in the *Student Guide.*
2. Assign Part 5 of the Home Practice.

Assessment

Use homework *Questions 1 and 9* in the *Student Guide* as an assessment.

Notes:

Student Guide

Questions 1–8 (SG pp. 310–312)

1. A. *Answers will vary. Students might say that it will save time, that you don't need as much space on your paper, or that it is more accurate.

    B. *1000s

    C. *1469

2. A. * $\boxed{1140} \boxed{\div} \boxed{24} \boxed{=}$

    B. $47.50

    C. *47 whole dollars

    D. *50¢ per classroom

    E. *Answers will vary. The remainder is a decimal that can be read as cents.

3. $\boxed{2489} \boxed{\div} \boxed{76} \boxed{=}$, $32.75, 32 whole dollars and 75¢ for each book

4. $\boxed{650} \boxed{\div} \boxed{52} \boxed{=}$, $12.50, 12 dollars and 50¢ per pizza

5. * $\boxed{5.00} \boxed{\div} \boxed{3} \boxed{=}$, $1.66, 1 dollar and 66¢ for each student with two pennies remaining

6. A. *19.25

    B. *19 whole boxes of cookies

    C. *0.25 or $\frac{1}{4}$ of one box is filled

    D. *228 cookies

7. A. 22 full boxes; $542 \div 24 = 22.58333$ (or R14); The number to the left of the decimal shows that 22 boxes were completely filled. The numbers to the right of the decimal show that only part of another box was filled.

    B. 14 muffins did not get packaged. $24 \times 22 = 528$; $542 - 528 = 14$

8. A. 268 full boxes; $38,664 \div 144 = 268.5$ (or R72); The number to the left of the decimal shows that 268 boxes will be completely filled. The numbers to the right of the decimal show that only part of another box was filled.

    B. 72 pencils; $144 \times 268 = 38,592$; $38,664 - 38,592 = 72$

Homework (SG pp. 312–313)

Questions 1–10

Estimates for *Questions 1–4* will vary. One answer is given.

1. 500; 531 R11

2. 3000; 2884 R32

3. 4000; 4224 R18

4. 600; 595

5. A. 69 full pages

    B. 5 stamps

6. A. 31 pieces

    B. 12 inches

7. 528 lights

8. $62.50

9. $1.67

10. 7 peanuts

Discovery Assignment Book

**Home Practice (DAB p. 150)

Part 5. Solving Problems

Questions 1–7

1. There is a total of 1152 pencils. Each classroom will get 38 pencils. 12 pencils will be left over for the office.

2. 41 journals. There will be one sheet of paper left over.

3. 8 of each table.

4. 26 burritos

5. 16 rows 2 chairs left over

6. A. 22 boxes

    B. 6 egg rolls

    C. $\frac{1}{2}$ an egg roll

7. A. 9 pages   B. 10 pages

*Answers and/or discussion are included in the Lesson Guide.

**Answers for all the Home Practice in the *Discovery Assignment Book* are at the end of the unit.

Q. Dividing by Multiples of Ten **N**
(URG p. 18)

A. $9000 \div 100 =$

B. $45,000 \div 900 =$

C. $20,000 \div 2 =$

D. $350 \div 70 =$

E. $250,000 \div 500 =$

F. $30,000 \div 30 =$

S. Reviewing Division Facts:
5s and 10s (URG p. 19)

A. $45 \div 5 =$ B. $25 \div 5 =$

C. $10 \div 2 =$ D. $60 \div 10 =$

E. $40 \div 8 =$ F. $30 \div 3 =$

G. $20 \div 5 =$ H. $80 \div 10 =$

I. $30 \div 6 =$ J. $35 \div 5 =$

K. $15 \div 3 =$ L. $50 \div 10 =$

M. $70 \div 10 =$ N. $90 \div 9 =$

O. $40 \div 4 =$ P. $20 \div 2 =$

Q. $100 \div 10 =$

DPP Task and Challenge are on page 81. Suggestions for using the DPPs are on page 81.

LESSON GUIDE 6

Grass Act

> **Estimated Class Sessions: 2**

This assessment is an open-ended problem that asks students to estimate the number of blades of grass in a specified area. Students use sampling in order to make their estimates. First students use a vignette in the *Student Guide* as a context for working with a group to develop a plan for solving the problem. Then students collect data and use the data to solve the problem and write about their solutions.

Key Content

- Solving open-ended problems and communicating solution strategies.
- Developing number sense for large numbers.
- Collecting and using data to solve problems.
- Averaging.
- Measuring area.
- Solving problems involving multiplication.
- Using the *Solving, Knowing,* and *Telling* Rubics to self-assess problem-solving skills.

Curriculum Sequence

Before This Unit

Sampling. In Unit 1 students used sampling procedures in the labs *Eyelets* and *Searching the Forest.* In Unit 2 students read the Adventure Book *Sand Reckoning.* In the story Archimedes used sampling to estimate the number of grains of sand it would take to fill the universe. You may want to review this story before beginning this assessment activity.

Open-ended problems. Students have solved several open-ended problems during the year. In Unit 2, students used number patterns and estimation to complete the problem *Stack Up* in Lesson 9. In Unit 8, they analyzed data and then used the data to make predictions in Lesson 4 *Florence Kelley's Report.*

Open-ended problems. Students will continue to solve open-ended problems in labs in succeeding units. Unit 11 Lesson 7 and Unit 16 Lesson 5 also provide opportunities to solve open-ended problems and communicate solution strategies.

Materials List

Print Materials for Students

		Math Facts and Daily Practice and Problems	Assessment Activity	Written Assessment
Student Book	**Student Guide**		*Grass Act* Page 314 and Student Rubrics: *Solving*, Appendix B; *Telling*, Appendix C (optional); and *Knowing*, Appendix A (optional); Inside Back Cover ◎	
Teacher Resources	**Facts Resource Guide** ◎	DPP Items 9Q and 9S		
	Unit Resource Guide	DPP Items Q–T Pages 18–20 ◎		*Grass Act Questions* Page 83, 1 per student and DPP Item T *Remainders* Page 20 ◎

◎ *available on Teacher Resource CD*

All Transparency Masters, Blackline Masters, and Assessment Blackline Masters in the Unit Resource Guide are on the Teacher Resource CD.

Supplies for Each Student

calculator
3" by 5" index card

Supplies for Each Student Group

scissors
ruler

Materials for the Teacher

TIMS Multidimensional Rubric (Teacher Implementation Guide, Assessment section)
poster or transparency of Student Rubric: *Solving;* Student Rubric: *Knowing;* Student Rubric: *Telling* (Teacher Implementation Guide, Assessment section), optional
a large grassy area on the playground or one of the following alternatives: piece of sod, nylon netting, window screen, or a large beach towel

Before the Activity

This assessment activity asks students to estimate the number of blades of grass in a given area. Choose an appropriate section of the school yard or nearby park. For the number of blades of grass to be in the millions, an area greater than 20 sq yd is needed. (This estimate is based on student-collected data. If a square inch of grass has about 40 blades of grass, then 20 sq yd of grass will have about 1,000,000 blades of grass. The number of blades of grass per square inch will vary from lawn to lawn.)

If your school does not have access to grass, four alternatives are outlined below.

1. If you have a grassy lawn to use as your representative area, but are not comfortable with taking students outside, consider bringing a piece of sod into the classroom. The children can do their sampling with the sod and the experience can be nearly as rich. Give students the area of the section of lawn in square yards or square feet, then ask them to estimate the number of blades of grass in the lawn. Alternatively, students can solve this problem:

   • *If the classroom floor were covered with grass, how many blades of grass would there be in the classroom?*

You may choose to use one of the three man-made alternatives in this activity: estimating the number of loops on a towel, holes in a screen, or holes in nylon netting. However, the numbers will not be quite as large or the magnitude of the amounts as visually accessible. To actually show a number well into the millions, many feet of towel, screen, or netting are needed.

2. Nylon netting is an inexpensive alternative for this activity. Found in most fabric stores, one yard of netting that is 72 inches wide has about 200,000 holes. Five yards of netting provides a good, concrete look at just over 1 million holes. Ask:

   • *How many holes are in the nylon netting?*

3. Another alternative, though slightly more costly, is window screen. A piece of screen $7\frac{1}{2}$ feet square will have about 1 million holes. If you choose to use window screen for this activity, look for plastic or fiberglass screen instead of metal to prevent accidental cuts. Ask:

   • *How many holes are in the screen?*

4. A final alternative is a towel. The loops which make up the pile are a little trickier to count, but possible. A typical hand towel measuring 15 inches by 20 inches will have about 100,000 loops. Ask:

   • *How many loops are on the towel?*

This Lesson Guide is written as if the activity will be completed using grass on a lawn. If you choose to use an alternative activity, adjust your lesson plans accordingly.

Developing the Activity

Part 1. Developing a Plan

Read the *Grass Act* Activity Page in the *Student Guide* so that students understand the context of the problem. After reading the exchange between Manny and Felicia, students work together in groups to develop a plan that will determine the number of grass blades in a lawn *(Question 1)*.

Before students begin working on their plans, review the rubrics that will be used to assess their work. We recommend that you assess students' written plans using the *Solving* Rubric. Encourage students to use the student rubrics as self-assessment tools as they write their plans. You can also review the Student Rubrics: *Knowing* and *Telling*. Then, assess their knowledge of skills and concepts and their abilities to communicate mathematically using those dimensions.

Although students develop their plans collaboratively with their groups, each student should record his or her plan independently *(Question 2)*. Groups should work without consulting you and rely instead on the members of their groups to help them with their questions. If a group needs additional help from you to get started, make notes of this so that you can include this information in your evaluation.

Student plans should include:

• finding the total area of the lawn;

• counting the blades of grass in several sample areas from the lawn;

• finding the average number of blades of grass in the samples; and

• using this average to estimate the number of blades of grass in the larger area.

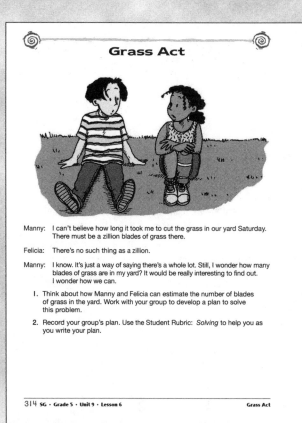

Grass Act

Manny: I can't believe how long it took me to cut the grass in our yard Saturday. There must be a zillion blades of grass there.

Felicia: There's no such thing as a zillion.

Manny: I know. It's just a way of saying there's a whole lot. Still, I wonder how many blades of grass are in my yard? It would be really interesting to find out. I wonder how we can.

1. Think about how Manny and Felicia can estimate the number of blades of grass in the yard. Work with your group to develop a plan to solve this problem.

2. Record your group's plan. Use the Student Rubric: *Solving* to help you as you write your plan.

314 SG · Grade 5 · Unit 9 · Lesson 6   Grass Act

Student Guide - Page 314

TIMS Tip

You may want to remind students about the Adventure Book *Sand Reckoning* at this time.

If students have difficulty devising a plan, review the sampling strategy used in *Sand Reckoning.* Ask students to think about how they can use sampling to estimate the number of blades of grass in a given area. Encourage students to choose an appropriate sample size such as a square inch.

Part 2. Solving the Problem

Once each group has completed the questions in the *Student Guide,* distribute the *Grass Act Questions* Assessment Page from the *Unit Resource Guide.* Identify the questions students must answer. Students should work in their groups to collect the data, then they should work independently to calculate their estimates and explain their strategies.

Students may choose different procedures for isolating a sample. One possible method is to use a note card with a square-inch hole removed to isolate a square inch "sample" of grass to count.

Once students have solved the problem and completed their writing, review their work for possible revisions. Then score their work using the dimensions of the rubric you chose.

Students can add their papers to their collection folders for possible inclusion in their portfolios. Encourage students to compare their work on this problem with similar problems from earlier in the year to see their growth in problem solving in fifth grade. This work can be compared to problems such as *Stack Up* from Unit 2 and *Florence Kelley's Report* from Unit 8.

To assist you in scoring student work, specific questions for each of the three dimensions of the *TIMS Multidimensional Rubric* are listed here:

Solving

- Did students clearly understand the relationship between the elements of this problem? For example, did they understand the relationship between the total area of the lawn and the sample size?

- Did students use efficient problem-solving strategies? For example, did they choose an appropriate sample size? Did they choose a practical method for converting square inches to square feet (or square yards)?

- Did they understand that an exact answer is not possible and choose efficient strategies to find an estimate?

- Did students organize their information? For example, did they record the counts from each sample? Did they organize their work using pictures or tables?

- Did they relate this problem to previously encountered mathematics? For example, did they use sampling as an estimation technique? Did they take multiple samples to get a more accurate estimate? Did they use averages as a way to "even out" the numbers in their samples?

- Did students work until they reached a solution? Did they solve the problem a second way as a check on their first solution?

- Did they look back to see if their solutions were reasonable?

Knowing

- Did students understand the task's mathematical concepts and apply them accurately? For example, did they know they needed to convert between square yards and square inches? Did they know how to use a sampling technique? Did they take multiple samples?

- Did students translate between words, pictures, symbols, and real situations? For example, did they draw a picture of the regions they sampled along with the whole area? Did they clearly explain their procedures in symbols and words?

- Did students use the tools of mathematics accurately? For example, did they use their calculators correctly? Did they measure correctly?

- Did students use their knowledge of mathematics to solve this problem? For example, did they find the average accurately? Did they convert between square yards and square inches correctly? Did they compute accurately when estimating the number of blades of grass in the total area?

Telling

- Were students' explanations clear and concise? Did they include each step of their plans? Did they clearly explain how they estimated the total number of blades of grass?

- Did students present supporting arguments for their conclusions? For example, did they show more than one way to arrive at the solution?

- Did students use pictures, symbols, or tables to clarify the explanation? Did they use correct number sentences in their explanations? Did they include diagrams or tables?

- Did students use correct terminology? For example, did students use square inches or square feet when discussing the area?

Sample student work follows. Student A estimated the total number of blades of grass in a portion of a playground. Student B estimated the number of holes in a window screen. Their work has been scored using all three dimensions of the *TIMS Multidimensional Rubric.*

Student A's work:

STEP 1: first we found a grassy spot to start at.

STEP 2: Then we used a toothpick to pull up the blades of grass and counted them with it.

STEP 3: Then we measured the section gvrs. miltrew marked off. (we used yards.)

STEP 4: Then we wrote down the data we collected and did all of our math. we used multiplaction and additions (11yrd and 16" and 10yrds and 21".)

STEPS IN OUR MATH,
first we did, 10 times 36 because there are 36" in a yrd. then we added 21" to that because there was still 21" left over and that was 381. Then we multiplyed 11 times 36 because there are 36" in a yrd. and then added 16" because there was 16 inches left and that was 412. Then we multiplyed 412 and 381 together and got 156,972. Then we multiplyed 156,972 by 31 because we got 31 in a sq. inch and got 4,866,132 blades of grass in the section my teacher marked off.

$$
\begin{array}{r}
36 \text{ inches} \\
\times 11 \text{ yds} \\
\hline
36 \\
+360 \\
\hline
396 \text{ inches}
\end{array}
\qquad
\begin{array}{r}
396 \text{ inches} \\
+16 \text{ inches} \\
\hline
412 \text{ inches}
\end{array}
$$

$$
\begin{array}{r}
412 \text{ inches} \\
\times 381 \text{ inches} \\
\hline
1412 \\
32960 \\
+123600 \\
\hline
156,972 \text{ inches}
\end{array}
\qquad
\begin{array}{r}
156,972 \text{ inches} \\
\times 31 \text{ blades of grass} \\
\hline
156972 \\
4709160 \\
\hline
4866,132 \text{ blades of grass}
\end{array}
$$

1. Answer: 4,866,132 blades of grass.

Student A's work scored on the *TIMS Multidimensional Rubric*:

Solving	Level 4	Level 3	(Level 2)	Level 1
Identifies the elements of the problem and their relationships to one another	All major elements identified	Most elements identified	(Some) but shows little understand- ing of relationships	Few or none
Uses problem-solving strategies which are…	Systematic, com- plete, efficient, and possibly elegant	(Systematic and nearly complete, but not efficient)	Incomplete or unsystematic	Not evident or inappropriate
Organizes relevant information…	Systematically and efficiently	(Systematically, with minor errors)	Unsystematically	Not at all
Relates the problem and solution to previously encountered mathematics and makes connections that are…	At length, elegant, and meaningful	Evident	(Brief) or logically unsound	Not evident
Persists in the problem-solving process…	At length	Until a solution is reached	Briefly	Not at all
Looks back to examine the reasonableness of the solution and draws conclusions that are…	Insightful and comprehensive	Correct	Incorrect or logically unsound	Not present

Knowing	Level 4	(Level 3)	Level 2	Level 1
Understands the task's mathematical concepts, their properties and applications…	Completely	Nearly completely	Partially	Not at all
Translates between words, pictures, symbols, tables, graphs, and real situations…	Readily and without errors	With minor errors	With major errors	Not at all
Uses tools (measuring devices, graphs, tables, calculators, etc.) and procedures…	Correctly and efficiently	(Correctly or with minor errors)	Incorrectly	Not at all
Uses knowledge of the facts of mathematics (geometry definitions, math facts, etc.)…	Correctly	With minor errors	With major errors	Not at all

Telling	Level 4	(Level 3)	Level 2	Level 1
Includes response with an explanation and/or description which is…	Complete and clear	Fairly complete and clear	Perhaps ambiguous or unclear	Totally unclear or irrelevant
Presents supporting arguments which are…	Strong and sound	Logically sound, but may contain minor gaps	Incomplete or logically unsound	Not present
Uses pictures, symbols, tables, and graphs which are…	Correct and clearly relevant	Present with minor errors or some- what irrelevant	Present with errors and/or irrelevant	Not present or completely inappropriate
Uses terminology…	Clearly and precisely	With minor errors	With major errors	Not at all

Figure 16: *Student A's work and scores on the rubrics*

Solving

Student A scored a 2 on the Solving dimension. She only partially understood the sampling procedure since she only took one sample. Therefore, she did not relate the problem to earlier labs in which the students made multiple trials. Furthermore, she did not understand that an estimate is all that is needed and that an exact answer is not possible. She organized her calculations and showed us her solution. However, she did not give any evidence that she tried to solve the problem in more than one way or look back at her answer to see if it was reasonable.

Knowing

Student A received a 3 on this dimension. She only partially understood the task, since she did not make multiple trials in her sampling procedure nor did she use more efficient estimation techniques appropriate to this problem. She translated the problems correctly into symbols, although she did not label her numbers correctly since she did not discriminate between inches and square inches. Her measurements are correct.

Telling

Since Student A's writing was fairly complete and clear, she scored a 3 on the Telling dimension. She used symbols to show her work correctly although she did not label them with the correct units. She did not use the correct terminology for inches and square inches nor draw a diagram of the solution.

Content Note

Choosing Appropriate Estimation Methods. Since the calculations in this lesson are estimates, it is appropriate to round numbers to ease computation. For example, Student A could have rounded the number of blades of grass in the sample to 30 blades of grass per square inch and rounded the number of square inches in the grassy area to 150,000 sq in. To find the estimate, she could have simply multiplied $30 \times 150,000$ to get an estimate of 4,500,000 blades of grass.

Student B's work:

We all make an estimation w/ index cards on how many holes their are in square inches in the screen then we add the estimates and divide by 5 to get the average. Then we figure out how many square inches are in the screen. We multiply the average times how many square inches in the screen and get our answer.

Estimates
18-324
17-289
16-256
14-196
15-225
÷ 1290
    5

Average = 258   sq. in
      × 860   43 inches × 20 inches = 860
    221,880

The holes in a screen

1. We cut a square inch out of an index card.

2. Then we put it on the screen and counted the holes in one row. then multiplyed the number twice.

3. we added our estimations together and divided the number by 5 because there are 5 estimations. That is our average 258

4. we measured two of the sides on the screen and multiplyd them together to find out how many square inches there are in the screen

5. Then we multipiyed the square inches by the average we got the answer.

6. the answer is 221,880

that is our estimation we got for how many holes there are in the screen.

Student B's work scored on the *TIMS Multidimensional Rubric:*

Solving	Level 4	Level 3	Level 2	Level 1
Identifies the elements of the problem and their relationships to one another	All major elements identified	Most elements identified	Some, but shows little understanding of relationships	Few or none
Uses problem-solving strategies which are…	Systematic, complete, efficient, and possibly elegant	Systematic and nearly complete, but not efficient	Incomplete or unsystematic	Not evident or inappropriate
Organizes relevant information…	Systematically and efficiently	Systematically, with minor errors	Unsystematically	Not at all
Relates the problem and solution to previously encountered mathematics and makes connections that are…	At length, elegant, and meaningful	Evident	Brief or logically unsound	Not evident
Persists in the problem-solving process…	At length	Until a solution is reached	Briefly	Not at all
Looks back to examine the reasonableness of the solution and draws conclusions that are…	Insightful and comprehensive	Correct	Incorrect or logically unsound	Not present

Knowing	Level 4	Level 3	Level 2	Level 1
Understands the task's mathematical concepts, their properties and applications…	Completely	Nearly completely	Partially	Not at all
Translates between words, pictures, symbols, tables, graphs, and real situations…	Readily and without errors	With minor errors	With major errors	Not at all
Uses tools (measuring devices, graphs, tables, calculators, etc.) and procedures…	Correctly and efficiently	Correctly or with minor errors	Incorrectly	Not at all
Uses knowledge of the facts of mathematics (geometry definitions, math facts, etc.)…	Correctly	With minor errors	With major errors	Not at all

Telling	Level 4	Level 3	Level 2	Level 1
Includes response with an explanation and/or description which is…	Complete and clear	Fairly complete and clear	Perhaps ambiguous or unclear	Totally unclear or irrelevant
Presents supporting arguments which are…	Strong and sound	Logically sound, but may contain minor gaps	Incomplete or logically unsound	Not present
Uses pictures, symbols, tables, and graphs which are…	Correct and clearly relevant	Present with minor errors or somewhat irrelevant	Present with errors and/or irrelevant	Not present or completely inappropriate
Uses terminology…	Clearly and precisely	With minor errors	With major errors	Not at all

Figure 17: *Student B's work and scores on the rubrics*

Solving

Student B scored a 3 on the Solving dimension. His group understood the sampling procedure, including taking multiple samples and finding the average. He also clearly understood how to find the area of the screen. However, he did not understand that an exact answer is not possible and convenient numbers would be more efficient. Student B persisted in the problem-solving process only until a solution was reached and he did not try to find a second strategy or check his answer to see if it is reasonable.

Knowing

Student B scored a 4 on this dimension. He understood the sampling task and he was able to measure and compute correctly. However, he did not always label the numbers in his explanations correctly, and he did not take advantage of more efficient round numbers.

Telling

Student B's writing was fairly complete and clear, so he earned a 3. We understand how he arrived at his solution, although his description of counting the holes in the screen is somewhat unclear. He uses the division sign in his explanation of finding an average in a nontraditional way, and he did not always label the numbers in the problem correctly.

Suggestions for Teaching the Lesson

Math Facts

DPP items Q and S practice the division facts for the 5s and 10s. DPP Bit Q provides practice dividing round numbers.

Homework and Practice

- Assign the Journal Prompt as a homework assignment.
- Assign DPP Task R which involves division, number sense, and an understanding of remainders.

Assessment

DPP Challenge T can be used to assess fluency in writing remainders as mixed numbers and decimals as well as interpreting remainders.

Daily Practice and Problems:
Task and Challenge for Lesson 6

R. Task: Thinking about Remainders (URG p. 19)

1. You are dividing a number by 6 and at the end of the problem your remainder is 7. What does that mean?

2. Make a list of the possible remainders you can have when you are finished dividing a number by 8.

T. Challenge: Remainders (URG p. 20)

1. Solve each of the following problems. Each one has a remainder. Write the quotient three ways: with a whole number remainder, as a mixed number, and as a decimal.

   A. $6 \div 4 =$ B. $19 \div 4 =$

   C. $49 \div 4 =$

2. Choose one of the problems. Write 3 different stories for the problem showing how you might use each of the three types of quotients.

📓 Journal Prompt
Explain how you might use a sampling strategy to estimate the number of people in a large crowd.

AT A GLANCE

Math Facts and Daily Practice and Problems

DPP items Q and S practice the facts for the 5s and 10s. Items R and T review division and remainders.

Part 1. Developing a Plan

1. Read and discuss the *Grass Act* Activity Page in the *Student Guide.*
2. Review the student rubrics that will be used to assess student work.
3. Students in small groups develop a plan for estimating the number of blades of grass on a lawn. *(Question 1)*
4. Each student records the group's plan independently. *(Question 2)*

Part 2. Solving the Problem

1. Distribute the *Grass Act Questions* Assessment Page from the *Unit Resource Guide.* Tell students which question they are to answer.
2. Students work in groups to collect data needed to solve the problem.
3. Students work independently to find an estimate for the number of blades of grass (holes or loops) in the area of study.
4. Teacher provides feedback on student work.
5. Students revise their work based on teacher input.
6. Students' work is scored using the *TIMS Multidimensional Rubric.* This work is then compared to other problems completed earlier in the year.

Homework

Assign the Journal Prompt for homework.

Assessment

Use DPP Challenge T as an assessment of concepts learned in this unit.

Notes:

Grass Act Questions

Your teacher will tell you which of the following problems to solve. After you have solved the problem, explain your solution.

1. Estimate the number of blades of grass in the lawn.

2. Estimate the number of holes in the nylon netting.

3. Estimate the number of holes in the screen.

4. Estimate the number of loops on the towel.

Unit Resource Guide

Grass Act Questions (URG p. 83)

Questions 1–4

*See Lesson Guide 6 for sample student work and scoring on all three student rubrics.

*Answers and/or discussion are included in the Lesson Guide.
**Answers for all the Home Practice in the *Discovery Assignment Book* are at the end of the unit.

Discovery Assignment Book

Part 1. Division Practice

Questions A–D (DAB p. 147)

A. 720 R2

Possible strategy: $5762 \div 8 \approx 5600 \div 8$ or 700

B. 140 R3

C. 1563 R2

D. 1063

Part 2. Fractions and Decimals

Questions 1–2 (DAB p. 147)

1. A. $\frac{7}{15} = \frac{21}{45}$ B. $\frac{3}{5} = \frac{27}{45}$

   C. $\frac{1}{3} = \frac{11}{33}$ D. $\frac{6}{16} = \frac{66}{176}$

2. A. 0.8, 80%   B. 0.58, 58%

   C. 0.27, 27%

Part 3. Multiplication and Division Practice

Questions A–I (DAB p. 148)

A. 2835   B. 36 R5

C. 1015   D. 365 R11

E. 0.26   F. 17

G. 22.41   H. 300

I. 187 R28

Part 4. Using Remainders

Questions 1–5 (DAB p. 149)

1. 8 runs

2. 4 pretzels

3. 12.5 feet or $12\frac{1}{2}$ feet

4. 13 cars

5. A. $28\frac{5}{15}$ or $28\frac{1}{3}$

   B. 70

   C. $222\frac{9}{18}$ or $222\frac{1}{2}$

Part 5. Solving Problems

Questions 1–7 (DAB p. 150)

1. There is a total of 1152 pencils. Each classroom will get 38 pencils. 12 pencils will be left over for the office.

2. 41 journals. There will be one sheet of paper left over.

3. 8 of each table.

4. 26 burritos

5. 16 rows 2 chairs left over

6. A. 22 boxes

   B. 6 egg rolls

   C. $\frac{1}{2}$ an egg roll

7. A. 9 pages   B. 10 pages

*Answers and/or discussion are included in the Lesson Guide.